· Childe Rowland ·

English Fairy Tales

Collected by
JOSEPH JACOBS

Illustrated by
JOHN D. BATTEN

Dover Publications, Inc.
New York

To my dear little May

Published in Canada by General Publishing Company, Ltd., 30 Lesmill Road, Don Mills, Toronto, Ontario.

Published in the United Kingdom by Constable and Company, Ltd., 10 Orange Street, London WC 2.

This Dover edition, first published in 1967, is an unabridged and unaltered republication of the third edition, as published by G. P. Putnam's Sons and David Nutt in 1898.

The publisher is grateful to the Director of the Haverford College Library for supplying a copy of this work for reproduction.

Standard Book Number: 486-21818-X
Library of Congress Catalog Card Number: 67-19703

Manufactured in the United States of America
Dover Publications, Inc.
180 Varick Street
New York, N.Y. 10014

Preface

WHO says that English folk have no fairy-tales of their own? The present volume contains only a selection out of some 140, of which I have found traces in this country. It is probable that many more exist.

A quarter of the tales in this volume, have been collected during the last ten years or so, and some of them have not been hitherto published. Up to 1870 it was equally said of France and of Italy, that they possessed no folk-tales. Yet, within fifteen years from that date, over 1000 tales had been collected in each country. I am hoping that the present volume may lead to equal activity in this country, and would earnestly beg any reader of this book who knows of similar tales, to communicate them, written down as they are told, to me, care of Mr. Nutt. The only reason, I imagine, why such tales have not hitherto been brought to light, is the lamentable gap between the governing and recording classes and the dumb working classes of this country—dumb to others but eloquent among themselves. It would be no unpatriotic task to help to bridge over this gulf, by giving a common fund of nursery literature to all classes of the English people, and, in any case, it can do no harm to add to the innocent gaiety of the nation.

A word or two as to our title seems necessary. We have called our stories Fairy Tales though few of them speak of fairies.* The same remark applies to the collection of the Brothers Grimm and to all the other European collections, which contain exactly the same classes of tales as ours. Yet our stories are what the little ones mean when they clamour for "Fairy Tales," and this is the only name which they give to them. One cannot imagine a child saying, "Tell us a folk-tale, nurse," or "Another nursery tale, please, grandma." As our book is intended for the little ones, we have indicated its contents by the name they use. The words "Fairy Tales" must accordingly be taken to include tales in which occurs something "fairy," something extraordinary—fairies, giants, dwarfs, speaking animals. It must be taken also to cover tales in which what is extraordinary is the stupidity of some of the actors. Many of the tales in this volume, as in similar collections for other European countries, are what the folk-lorists call Drolls. They

* For some recent views on fairies and tales *about* fairies, see Notes, pp. 241-4.

serve to justify the title of Merrie England, which used to be given to this country of ours, and indicate unsuspected capacity for fun and humour among the unlettered classes. The story of Tom Tit Tot, which opens our collection, is unequalled among all other folk-tales I am acquainted with, for its combined sense of humour and dramatic power.

The first adjective of our title also needs a similar extension of its meaning. I have acted on Molière's principle, and have taken what was good wherever I could find it. Thus, a couple of these stories have been found among descendants of English immigrants in America; a couple of others I tell as I heard them myself in my youth in Australia. One of the best was taken down from the mouth of an English Gipsy. I have also included some stories that have only been found in Lowland Scotch. I have felt justified in doing this, as of the twenty-one folk-tales contained in Chambers' "Popular Rhymes of Scotland," no less than sixteen are also to be found in an English form. With the Folk-tale as with the Ballad Lowland Scotch may be regarded as simply a dialect of English, and it is a mere chance whether a tale is extant in one or other, or both.

I have also rescued and re-told a few Fairy Tales that only exist now-a-days in the form of ballads. There are certain indications that the " common form " of the English Fairy Tale was the *cante-fable*, a mixture of narrative and verse of which the most illustrious example in literature is

" Aucassin et Nicolette." In one case I have endeavoured to retain this form, as the tale in which it occurs, " Childe Rowland," is mentioned by Shakespeare in *King Lear*, and is probably, as I have shown, the source of Milton's *Comus*. Late as they have been collected, some dozen of the tales can be traced back to the sixteenth century, two of them being quoted by Shakespeare himself.

In the majority of instances I have had largely to re-write* these Fairy Tales, especially those in dialect, including the Lowland Scotch. Children, and sometimes those of larger growth, will not read dialect. I have also had to reduce the flatulent phraseology of the eighteenth-century chap-books, and to re-write in simpler style the stories only extant in " Literary " English. I have, however, left a few vulgarisms in the mouths of vulgar people. Children appreciate the dramatic propriety of this as much as their elders. Generally speaking, it has been my ambition to write as a good old nurse will speak when she tells Fairy Tales. I am doubtful as to my success in catching the colloquial-romantic tone appropriate for such narratives, but the thing had to be done or else my main object, to give a book of English Fairy Tales which English children will listen to, would have been unachieved.

* It is perhaps worth remarking that the Brothers Grimm did the same with their stories. "Dass der Ausdruck," say they in their Preface, " und die Ausführung des Einzelnen grossentheils von uns herrührt versteht sich von selbst." I may add that many of their stories were taken from printed sources. In the first volume of Mrs. Hunt's translation, Nos. 12, 18, 19, 23, 32, 35, 42, 43, 44, 69, 77, 78, 83, 89, are thus derived.

Preface

This book is meant to be read aloud, and not merely taken in by the eye.

In a few instances I have introduced or changed an incident. I have never done so, however, without mentioning the fact in the Notes. These have been relegated to the obscurity of small print and a back place, while the little ones have been, perhaps unnecessarily, warned off them. They indicate my sources and give a few references to parallels and variants which may be of interest to fellow-students of Folk-lore. It is, perhaps, not necessary to inform readers who are not fellow-students that the study of Folk-tales has pretensions to be a science. It has its special terminology, and its own methods of investigation, by which it is hoped, one of these days, to gain fuller knowledge of the workings of the popular mind as well as traces of archaic modes of thought and custom. I hope on some future occasion to treat the subject of the English Folk-tale on a larger scale and with all the necessary paraphernalia of prolegomena and excursus. I shall then, of course, reproduce my originals with literal accuracy, and have therefore felt the more at liberty on the present occasion to make the necessary deviations from this in order to make the tales readable for children.

Finally, I have to thank those by whose kindness in waiving their rights to some of these stories, I have been enabled to compile this book. My friends Mr. E. Clodd, Mr. F. Hindes Groome, and Mr. Andrew Lang, have thus yielded up to me some of the most attractive stories in the following pages.   The Councils of the English and of the American Folk-lore Societies, and Messrs. Longmans, have also been equally generous.   Nor can I close these remarks without a word of thanks and praise to the artistic skill with which my friend, Mr. J. D. Batten, has made the romance and humour of these stories live again in the brilliant designs with which he has adorned these pages. It should be added that the dainty headpieces to "Henny Penny" and "Mr. Fox" are due to my old friend, Mr. Henry Ryland.

Prefatory Note to the Third Edition

I HAVE taken the opportunity of a fresh issue of this book to revise the phraseology and bring the Notes, as far as possible, up to date.   The remarkable cordiality with which the book has been received by readers, young and old, has laid upon me the obligation of making it as worthy as possible of such a kind reception.

JOSEPH JACOBS.

Jan. 1898

Contents

Contents

Full Page Illustrations

Tom Tit Tot

ONCE upon a time there was a woman, and she baked five pies. And when they came out of the oven, they were that overbaked the crusts were too hard to eat. So she says to her daughter :

"Darter," says she, "put you them there pies on the shelf, and leave 'em there a little, and they'll come again."—She meant, you know, the crust would get soft.

But the girl, she says to herself : "Well, if they'll come again, I'll eat 'em now." And she set to work and ate 'em all, first and last.

Well, come supper-time the woman said: "Go you, and get one o' them there pies. I dare say they've come again now."

The girl went and she looked, and there was nothing but the dishes. So back she came and says she : "Noo, they ain't come again."

"Not one of 'em ?" says the mother.

"Not one of 'em," says she.

" Well, come again, or not come again," said the woman,
" I'll have one for supper."

" But you can't, if they ain't come," said the girl.

" But I can," says she. " Go you, and bring the best
of 'em."

" Best or worst," says the girl, " I've ate 'em all, and
you can't have one till that's come again."

Well, the woman she was done, and she took her
spinning to the door to spin, and as she span she sang:

> " My darter ha' ate five, five pies to-day.
> My darter ha' ate five, five pies to-day."

The king was coming down the street, and he heard
her sing, but what she sang he couldn't hear, so he stopped
and said:

"What was that you were singing, my good woman?"

The woman was ashamed to let him hear what her
daughter had been doing, so she sang, instead of that:

> " My darter ha' spun five, five skeins to-day.
> My darter ha' spun five, five skeins to-day."

" Stars o' mine!" said the king, " I never heard tell of
any one that could do that."

Then he said: " Look you here, I want a wife, and I'll
marry your daughter. But look you here," says he, " eleven
months out of the year she shall have all she likes to eat,
and all the gowns she likes to get, and all the company
she likes to keep; but the last month of the year she'll
have to spin five skeins every day, and if she don't I shall
kill her."

" All right," says the woman; for she thought what a

grand marriage that was. And as for the five skeins, when the time came, there'd be plenty of ways of getting out of it, and likeliest, he'd have forgotten all about it.

Well, so they were married. And for eleven months the girl had all she liked to eat, and all the gowns she liked to get, and all the company she liked to keep.

But when the time was getting over, she began to think about the skeins and to wonder if he had 'em in mind. But not one word did he say about 'em, and she thought he'd wholly forgotten 'em.

However, the last day of the last month he takes her to a room she'd never set eyes on before. There was nothing in it but a spinning-wheel and a stool. And says he : "Now, my dear, here you'll be shut in to-morrow with some victuals and some flax, and if you haven't spun five skeins by the night, your head 'll go off."

And away he went about his business.

Well, she was that frightened, she'd always been such a gatless girl, that she didn't so much as know how to spin, and what was she to do to-morrow with no one to come nigh her to help her ? She sat down on a stool in the kitchen, and law ! how she did cry !

However, all of a sudden she heard a sort of a knocking low down on the door. She upped and oped it, and what should she see but a small little black thing with a long tail. That looked up at her right curious, and that said :

"What are you a-crying for ?"

"What's that to you ?" says she.

"Never you mind," that said, "but tell me what you're a-crying for."

"That won't do me no good if I do," says she.

"You don't know that," that said, and twirled that's tail round.

"Well," says she, "that won't do no harm, if that don't do no good," and she upped and told about the pies, and the skeins, and everything.

" This is what I'll do."

"This is what I'll do," says the little black thing, " I'll come to your window every morning and take the flax and bring it spun at night."

"What's your pay?" says she.

That looked out of the corner of that's eyes, and that said: "I'll give you three guesses every night to guess my name, and if you haven't guessed it before the month's up, you shall be mine."

Well, she thought she'd be sure to guess that's name before the month was up. "All right," says she, "I agree."

"All right," that says, and law! how that twirled that's tail.

Well, the next day, her husband took her into the room, and there was the flax and the day's food.

"Now there's the flax," says he, "and if that ain't spun up this night, off goes your head." And then he went out and locked the door.

He'd hardly gone, when there was a knocking against the window.

She upped and she oped it, and there sure enough was the little old thing sitting on the ledge.

"Where's the flax?" says he.

"Here it be," says she. And she gave it to him.

Well, come the evening a knocking came again to the window. She upped and she oped it, and there was the little old thing with five skeins of flax on his arm.

"Here it be," says he, and he gave it to her.

"Now, what's my name?" says he.

"What, is that Bill?" says she.

"Noo, that ain't," says he, and he twirled his tail.

"Is that Ned?" says she.

"Noo, that ain't," says he, and he twirled his tail.

"Well, is that Mark?" says she.

"Noo, that ain't," says he, and he twirled his tail harder, and away he flew.

Well, when her husband came in, there were the five skeins ready for him. "I see I shan't have to kill you to-night, my dear," says he; "you'll have your food and your flax in the morning," says he, and away he goes.

Well, every day the flax and the food were brought, and every day that there little black impet used to come mornings and evenings. And all the day the girl sate trying to think of names to say to it when it came at night. But she never hit on the right one. And as it got towards the end of the month, the impet began to look so maliceful, and that twirled that's tail faster and faster each time she gave a guess.

At last it came to the last day but one. The impet came at night along with the five skeins, and that said :

" What, ain't you got my name yet ? "

" Is that Nicodemus ? " says she.

" Noo, t'ain't," that says.

" Is that Sammle ? " says she.

" Noo, t'ain't," that says.

" A-well, is that Methusalem ? " says she.

" Noo, t'ain't that neither," that says.

Then that looks at her with that's eyes like a coal o' fire, and that says : " Woman, there's only to-morrow night, and then you'll be mine ! " And away it flew.

Well, she felt that horrid. However, she heard the king coming along the passage. In he came, and when he sees the five skeins, he says, says he :

" Well, my dear," says he. " I don't see but what you'll have your skeins ready to-morrow night as well, and as I reckon I shan't have to kill you, I'll have supper in here to-night." So they brought supper, and another stool for him, and down the two sate.

Well, he hadn't eaten but a mouthful or so, when he stops and begins to laugh.

"What is it?" says she.

"A-why," says he, "I was out a-hunting to-day, and I got away to a place in the wood I'd never seen before And there was an old chalk-pit. And I heard a kind of a sort of a humming. So I got off my hobby, and I went right quiet to the pit, and I looked down. Well, what should there be but the funniest little black thing you ever set eyes on. And what was that doing, but that had a little spinning-wheel, and that was spinning wonderful fast, and twirling that's tail. And as that span that sang:

> "Nimmy nimmy not
> My name's Tom Tit Tot."

Well, when the girl heard this, she felt as if she could have jumped out of her skin for joy, but she didn't say a word.

Next day that there little thing looked so maliceful when he came for the flax. And when night came, she heard that knocking against the window panes. She oped the window, and that come right in on the ledge. That was grinning from ear to ear, and Oo! that's tail was twirling round so fast.

"What's my name?" that says, as that gave her the skeins.

"Is that Solomon?" she says, pretending to be afeard.

"Noo, t'ain't," that says, and that come further into the room.

"Well, is that Zebedee?" says she again.

"Noo, 'tain't," says the impet. And then that laughed and twirled that's tail till you couldn't hardly see it.

"Take time, woman," that says; "next guess, and you're mine." And that stretched out that's black hands at her.

Well, she backed a step or two, and she looked at it, and then she laughed out, and says she, pointing her finger at it:

NIMMY NIMMY NOT

YOUR NAME'S TOM

TIT

TOT

Well, when that heard her, that gave an awful shriek and away that flew into the dark, and she never saw it any more.

The Three Sillies

ONCE upon a time there was a farmer and his wife who had one daughter, and she was courted by a gentleman. Every evening he used to come and see her, and stop to supper at the farmhouse, and the daughter used to be sent down into the cellar to draw the beer for supper. So one evening she had gone down to draw the beer, and she happened to look up at the ceiling while she was drawing, and she saw a mallet stuck in one of the beams. It must have been there a long, long time, but somehow or other she had never noticed it before, and she began a-thinking. And she thought it was very dangerous to have that mallet there, for she said to herself: "Suppose him and me was to be married, and we was to have a son, and he was to grow up to be a man, and come down into the cellar to draw the beer, like as I'm doing now, and the mallet was to fall on his head and kill him, what a dreadful thing it would be!" And she put down the candle and the jug, and sat herself down and began a-crying.

Well, they began to wonder upstairs how it was that

she was so long drawing the beer, and her mother went down to see after her, and she found her sitting on the settle crying, and the beer running over the floor. "Why, whatever is the matter?" said her mother. "Oh, mother!" says she, "look at that horrid mallet! Suppose we was to be married, and was to have a son, and he was to grow up, and was to come down to the cellar to draw the beer, and the mallet was to fall on his head and kill him, what a dreadful thing it would be!" "Dear, dear! what a dreadful thing it would be!" said the mother, and she sat her down aside of the daughter and started a-crying too. Then after a bit the father began to wonder that they didn't come back, and he went down into the cellar to look after them himself, and there they two sat a-crying, and the beer running all over the floor. "Whatever is the matter?" says he. "Why," says the mother, "look at that horrid mallet. Just suppose, if our daughter and her sweetheart was to be married, and was to have a son, and he was to grow up, and was to come down into the cellar to draw the beer, and the mallet was to fall on his head and kill him, what a dreadful thing it would be!" "Dear, dear, dear! so it would!" said the father, and he sat himself down aside of the other two, and started a-crying.

Now the gentleman got tired of stopping up in the kitchen by himself, and at last he went down into the cellar too, to see what they were after; and there they three sat a-crying side by side, and the beer running all over the floor. And he ran straight and turned the tap. Then he said: "Whatever are you three doing, sitting there crying, and letting the beer run all over the floor?"

"Oh!" says the father, "look at that horrid mallet! Suppose you and our daughter was to be married, and was to have a son, and he was to grow up, and was to come down into the cellar to draw the beer, and the mallet was to fall on his head and kill him!" And then they all started a-crying worse than before. But the gentleman burst out a-laughing, and reached up and pulled out the mallet, and then he said : "I've travelled many miles, and I never met three such big sillies as you three before ; and now I shall start out on my travels again, and when I can find three bigger sillies than you three, then I'll come back and marry your daughter." So he wished them good-bye, and started off on his travels, and left them all crying because the girl had lost her sweetheart.

Well, he set out, and he travelled a long way, and at last he came to a woman's cottage that had some grass growing on the roof. And the woman was trying to get her cow to go up a ladder to the grass, and the poor thing durst not go. So the gentleman asked the woman what she was doing. "Why, lookye," she said, "look at all that beautiful grass. I'm going to get the cow on to the roof to eat it. She'll be quite safe, for I shall tie a string round her neck, and pass it down the chimney, and tie it to my wrist as I go about the house, so she can't fall off without my knowing it." "Oh, you poor silly!" said the gentleman, "you should cut the grass and throw it down to the cow!" But the woman thought it was easier to get the cow up the ladder than to get the grass down, so she pushed her and coaxed her and got her up, and tied a string round her neck, and passed it down the chimney, and fastened it to her own wrist.   And the gentleman went on his way, but he hadn't gone far when the cow tumbled off the roof, and hung by the string tied round her neck, and it strangled her.   And the weight of the cow tied to her wrist pulled

the woman up the chimney, and she stuck fast half-way and was smothered in the soot.

Well, that was one big silly.

And the gentleman went on and on, and he went to an inn to stop the night, and they were so full at the inn that they had to put him in a double-bedded room, and another traveller was to sleep in the other bed. The other man was a very pleasant fellow, and they got very friendly together ; but in the morning, when they were both getting up, the gentleman was surprised to see the other hang his trousers on the knobs of the chest of drawers and run across the room and try to jump into them, and he tried over and over again, and couldn't manage it ; and the gentleman wondered whatever he was doing it for. At last he stopped and wiped his face with his handkerchief. "Oh dear," he says, " I do think trousers are the most awkwardest kind of clothes that ever were. I can't think who could have invented such things. It takes me the best part of an hour to get into mine every morning, and I get so hot! How do you manage yours ? " So the gentleman burst out a-laughing, and showed him how to put them on ; and he was very much obliged to him, and said he never should have thought of doing it that way.

So that was another big silly.

Then the gentleman went on his travels again ; and he came to a village, and outside the village there was a pond, and round the pond was a crowd of people. And they had got rakes, and brooms, and pitchforks, reaching into the pond ; and the gentleman asked what was the matter. "Why," they say, " matter enough! Moon's tumbled into the pond, and we can't rake her out any- how ! " So the gentleman burst out a-laughing, and told them to look up into the sky, and that it was only the shadow in the water. But they wouldn't listen to him, and abused him shamefully, and he got away as quick as he could.

So there was a whole lot of sillies bigger than them three sillies at home. So the gentleman turned back home again and married the farmer's daughter, and if they didn't live happy for ever after, that's nothing to do with you or me.

MY LIT-
-TLE
BRO-
-THER

WHOM
I
LOVE

SITS BE-
LOW

AND
I

SING
A-
-BOVE

The Rose-Tree

THERE was once upon a time a good man who had two children: a girl by a first wife, and a boy by the second. The girl was as white as milk, and her lips were like cherries. Her hair was like golden silk, and it hung to the ground. Her brother loved her dearly, but her wicked stepmother hated her. "Child," said the stepmother one day, "go to the grocer's shop and buy me a pound of candles." She gave her the money ; and the little girl went, bought the candles, and started on her return. There was a stile to cross. She put down the candles whilst she got over the stile. Up came a dog and ran off with the candles.

She went back to the grocer's, and she got a second bunch. She came to the stile, set down the candles, and proceeded to climb over. Up came the dog and ran off with the candles.

She went again to the grocer's, and she got a third bunch ; and just the same happened. Then she came to her stepmother crying, for she had spent all the money and had lost three bunches of candles.

The stepmother was angry, but she pretended not to mind the loss. She said to the child : "Come, lay your head on my lap that I may comb your hair." So the little one laid her head in the woman's lap, who proceeded to comb the yellow silken hair. And when she combed the hair fell over her knees, and rolled right down to the ground.

Then the stepmother hated her more for the beauty of her hair ; so she said to her, "I cannot part your hair on my knee, fetch a billet of wood." So she fetched it. Then said the stepmother, "I cannot part your hair with a comb, fetch me an axe." So she fetched it.

"Now," said the wicked woman, "lay your head down on the billet whilst I part your hair."

Well ! she laid down her little golden head without fear ; and whist ! down came the axe, and it was off. So the mother wiped the axe and laughed.

Then she took the heart and liver of the little girl, and she stewed them and brought them into the house for supper. The husband tasted them and shook his head. He said they tasted very strangely. She gave some to the little boy, but he would not eat. She tried to force him, but he refused, and ran out into the garden, and took up his little sister, and put her in a box, and buried the box under a rose-tree; and every day he went to the tree and wept, till his tears ran down on the box.

One day the rose-tree flowered. It was spring, and there among the flowers was a white bird; and it sang, and sang, and sang like an an angel out of heaven. Away it flew, and it went to a cobbler's shop, and perched itself on a tree hard by; and thus it sang :

> " My wicked mother slew me,
> My dear father ate me,
> My little brother whom I love
> Sits below, and I sing above
> Stick, stock, stone dead."

" Sing again that beautiful song," asked the shoemaker. " If you will first give me those little red shoes you are making." The cobbler gave the shoes, and the bird sang the song; then flew to a tree in front of a watchmaker's, and sang :

> " My wicked mother slew me,
> My dear father ate me,
> My little brother whom I love
> Sits below, and I sing above
> Stick, stock, stone dead."

" Oh, the beautiful song ! sing it again, sweet bird," asked the watchmaker. " If you will give me first that gold watch and chain in your hand." The jeweller gave the watch and chain. The bird took it in one foot, the shoes in the other, and, after having repeated the song, flew away to where three millers were picking a millstone. The bird perched on a tree and sang :

> " My wicked mother slew me,
> My dear father ate me,
> My little brother whom I love
> Sits below, and I sing above
> Stick !

Then one of the men put down his tool and and looked up from his work,
> " Stock !

Then the second miller's man laid aside his tool and looked up,
> " Stone !

Then the third miller's man laid down his tool and looked up,
> " Dead ! "

Then all three cried out with one voice : " Oh, what a beautiful song ! Sing it, sweet bird, again." " If you will put the millstone round my neck," said the bird. The men did what the bird wanted and away to the tree it flew with the millstone round its neck, the red shoes in one foot, and the gold watch and chain in the other. It sang the song and then flew home. It rattled the millstone against the eaves of the house, and the step-mother said : "It thunders." Then the little boy ran out to see the thunder, and down dropped the red shoes at his feet. It rattled the millstone against the eaves of the house once more, and the stepmother said again : " It thunders." Then the father ran out and down fell the chain about his neck.

In ran father and son, laughing and saying, "See, what fine things the thunder has brought us!" Then the bird rattled the millstone against the eaves of the house a third time; and the stepmother said : "It thunders again, perhaps the thunder has brought something for me," and she ran out ; but the moment she stepped outside the door, down fell the millstone on her head ; and so she died.

The Old Woman and her Pig

AN old woman was sweeping her house, and she found a little crooked sixpence. "What," said she, "shall I do with this little sixpence? I will go to market, and buy a little pig."

As she was coming home, she came to a stile: but the piggy wouldn't go over the stile.

She went a little further, and she met a dog. So she said to him! "Dog! dog, bite pig; piggy won't go over the stile; and I shan't get home to-night." But the dog wouldn't.

But the dog wouldn't.

She went a little further, and she met a stick. So she said : "Stick! stick! beat dog! dog won't bite pig; piggy won't get over the stile; and I shan't get home to-night." But the stick wouldn't.

She went a little further, and she met a fire. So she said : "Fire! fire! burn stick; stick won't beat dog; dog won't bite pig; piggy won't get over the stile; and I shan't get home to-night." But the fire wouldn't.

She went a little further, and she met some water. So she said : "Water, water! quench fire; fire won't burn stick; stick won't beat dog; dog won't bite pig; piggy won't get over the stile; and I shan't get home to-night." But the water wouldn't.

She went a little further, and she met an ox. So she said : "Ox! ox! drink water; water won't quench fire; fire won't burn stick; stick won't beat dog; dog won't bite pig; piggy won't get over the stile; and I shan't get home to-night." But the ox wouldn't.

She went a little further, and she met a butcher. So she said : "Butcher! butcher! kill ox; ox won't drink water; water won't quench fire; fire won't burn stick; stick won't beat dog; dog won't bite pig;

But the butcher wouldn't.

piggy won't get over the stile; and I shan't get home to-night." But the butcher wouldn't.

She went a little further, and she met a rope. So she said : "Rope! rope! hang butcher; butcher won't kill ox ; ox won't drink water ; water won't quench fire ; fire won't burn stick ; stick won't beat dog ; dog won't bite pig ; piggy won't get over the stile ; and I shan't get home to-night." But the rope wouldn't.

She went a little further, and she met a rat. So she said : "Rat ! rat ! gnaw rope ; rope won't hang butcher ; butcher won't kill ox ; ox won't drink water ; water won't quench fire ; fire won't burn stick ; stick won't beat dog ; dog won't bite pig ; piggy won't get over the stile ; and I shan't get home to-night." But the rat wouldn't.

She went a little further, and she met a cat. So she said : "Cat ! cat ! kill rat ; rat won't gnaw rope ; rope won't hang butcher ; butcher won't kill ox ; ox won't drink water ; water won't quench fire ; fire won't burn stick ; stick won't beat dog ; dog won't bite pig ; piggy won't get over the stile ; and I shan't get home to-night." But the cat said to her, "If you will go to yonder cow, and fetch me a saucer of milk, I will kill the rat." So away went the old woman to the cow.

But the cow said to her : "If you will go to yonder hay-stack, and fetch me a handful of hay, I'll give you the milk." So away went the old woman to the hay-stack ; and she brought the hay to the cow.

As soon as the cow had eaten the hay, she gave the old woman the milk ; and away she went with it in a saucer to the cat.

As soon as the cat had lapped up the milk, the cat began to kill the rat ; the rat began to gnaw the rope ; the rope began to hang the butcher ; the butcher began to kill the ox ; the ox began to drink the water ; the water began to quench the fire ; the fire began to burn the stick ; the stick began to beat the dog ; the dog began to bite the pig ; the little pig in a fright jumped over the stile ; and so the old woman got home that night.

How Jack Went to Seek his Fortune

How Jack went to Seek his Fortune

ONCE on a time there was a boy named Jack, and one morning he started to go and seek his fortune.

He hadn't gone very far before he met a cat.

"Where are you going, Jack?" said the cat.

"I am going to seek my fortune."

"May I go with you?"

"Yes," said Jack, "the more the merrier."

So on they went, jiggelty-jolt, jiggelty-jolt.

They went a little further and they met a dog.

"Where are you going, Jack?" said the dog.

"I am going to seek my fortune."

"May I go with you?"

"Yes," said Jack, "the more the merrier."

So on they went, jiggelty-jolt, jiggelty-jolt.

They went a little further and they met a goat.

"Where are you going, Jack?" said the goat,

"I am going to seek my fortune."

"May I go with you?"

"Yes," said Jack, "the more the merrier."

So on they went, jiggelty-jolt, jiggelty-jolt.

They went a little further and they met a bull.

"Where are you going, Jack?" said the bull.

"I am going to seek my fortune."

"May I go with you?"

"Yes," said Jack, "the more the merrier."

So on they went, jiggelty-jolt, jiggelty-jolt.

They went a little further and they met a rooster.

"Where are you going, Jack?" said the rooster.

"I am going to seek my fortune."

"May I go with you?"

"Yes," said Jack, "the more the merrier."

So on they went, jiggelty-jolt, jiggelty-jolt.

Well, they went on till it was about dark, and they began to think of some place where they could spend the night. About this time they came in sight of a house, and Jack told them to keep still while he went up and looked in through the window. And there were some robbers counting over their money. Then Jack went back and told them to wait till he gave the word, and then to make all the noise they could. So when they were all ready Jack gave the word, and the cat mewed, and the dog barked, and the goat bleated, and the bull bellowed, and the rooster crowed, and all together they made such a dreadful noise that it frightened the robbers all away.

And then they went in and took possession of the house. Jack was afraid the robbers would come back in the night, and so when it came time to go to bed he put the cat in the rocking-chair, and he put the dog under the table, and he put the goat upstairs, and he put the bull in the cellar, and the rooster flew up on to the roof, and Jack went to bed.

By-and-by the robbers saw it was all dark and they sent one man back to the house to look after their money. Before long he came back in a great fright and told them his story.

"I went back to the house," said he, "and went in and tried to sit down in the rocking-chair, and there was an old woman knitting, and she stuck her knitting-needles into me." That was the cat, you know.

"I went to the table to look after the money and there was a shoemaker under the table, and he stuck his awl into me." That was the dog, you know.

"I started to go upstairs, and there was a man up there threshing, and he knocked me down with his flail." That was the goat, you know.

"I started to go down cellar, and there was a man down there chopping wood, and he knocked me up with his axe." That was the bull, you know.

" But I shouldn't have minded all that if it hadn't been for that little fellow on top of the house, who kept a-hollering, ' Chuck him up to me-e !   Chuck him up to me-e !' "   Of course that was the cock-a-doodle-do.

Mr. Vinegar

MR. and Mrs. Vinegar lived in a vinegar bottle. Now, one day, when Mr. Vinegar was from home, Mrs. Vinegar, who was a very good housewife, was busily sweeping her house, when an unlucky thump of the broom brought the whole house clitter-clatter, clitter-clatter, about her ears. In an agony of grief she rushed forth to meet her husband. On seeing him she exclaimed, "Oh, Mr. Vinegar, Mr. Vinegar, we are ruined, we are ruined: I have knocked the house down, and it is all to pieces!" Mr. Vinegar then said: "My dear, let us see what can be done. Here is the door; I will take it on my back, and we will go forth to seek our fortune." They walked all that day, and at nightfall entered a thick forest. They were both very, very tired, and Mr. Vinegar said : "My love, I will climb up into a tree, drag up the door, and you shall follow." He accordingly did so, and they both stretched their weary limbs on the door, and fell fast asleep. In the middle of the night Mr. Vinegar was disturbed by the sound of voices underneath, and to his horror and dismay found that it was a band of thieves met to divide their booty. "Here, Jack," said one, "here's five pounds for you ; here, Bill, here's ten pounds for you ; here, Bob, here's three pounds for you." Mr. Vinegar could listen no longer ; his terror was so great that he trembled and trembled, and shook down the door on their heads. Away scampered the thieves, but Mr. Vinegar dared not quit his retreat till broad daylight. He then scrambled out of the tree, and went to lift up the door. What did he see but a number of golden guineas. "Come down, Mrs. Vinegar," he cried ; "come down, I say ; our fortune's made, our fortune's made ! Come down, I say." Mrs. Vinegar got down as fast as she could, and when she saw the money she jumped for joy. "Now, my dear," said she, "I'll tell you what you shall do. There is a fair at the neighbouring town ; you shall take these forty guineas and buy a cow. I can make butter and cheese, which you shall sell at market, and we shall then be able to live very comfortably." Mr. Vinegar joyfully agrees, takes the money, and off he goes to the fair. When he arrived, he walked up and down, and at length saw a beautiful red cow. It was an excellent milker, and perfect in every way. "Oh," thought Mr. Vinegar, "if I had but that cow, I should be the happiest man alive." So he offers the forty guineas for the cow, and

the owner said that, as he was a friend, he'd oblige him.
So the bargain was made, and he got the cow and he
drove it backwards and forwards to show it. By-and-by
he saw a man playing the bagpipes—Tweedle-dum
tweedle-dee. The children followed him about, and he
appeared to be pocketing money on all sides. "Well,"
thought Mr. Vinegar, "if I had but that beautiful
instrument I should be the happiest man alive—my
fortune would be made." So he went up to the man.
"Friend," says he, "what a beautiful instrument that is,
and what a deal of money you must make." "Why,
yes," said the man, "I make a great deal of money,
to be sure, and it is a wonderful instrument." "Oh!"
cried Mr. Vinegar, "how I should like to possess it!"
"Well," said the man, "as you are a friend, I don't
much mind parting with it; you shall have it for that
red cow." "Done!" said the delighted Mr. Vinegar.
So the beautiful red cow was given for the bagpipes.
He walked up and down with his purchase; but it was
in vain he tried to play a tune, and instead of pocketing pence, the boys followed him hooting, laughing,
and pelting.

Poor Mr. Vinegar, his fingers grew very cold, and,
just as he was leaving the town, he met a man with a
fine thick pair of gloves. "Oh, my fingers are so very
cold," said Mr. Vinegar to himself. "Now if I had but
those beautiful gloves I should be the happiest man
alive." He went up to the man, and said to him:
"Friend, you seem to have a capital pair of gloves there."
"Yes, truly," cried the man; "and my hands are as
warm as possible this cold November day." "Well," said

Mr. Vinegar, "I should like to have them." "What will you give?" said the man; "as you are a friend, I don't much mind letting you have them for those bag-pipes." "Done!" cried Mr. Vinegar. He put on the gloves, and felt perfectly happy as he trudged home-wards.

At last he grew very tired, when he saw a man coming towards him with a good stout stick in his hand.

"Oh," said Mr. Vinegar, "that I had but that stick! I should then be the happiest man alive." He said to the man: "Friend! what a rare good stick you have got." "Yes," said the man; "I have used it for many a long mile, and a good friend it has been; but if you have a fancy for it, as you are a friend, I don't mind giving it to you for that pair of gloves." Mr. Vinegar's hands were so warm, and his legs so tired, that he gladly made the exchange. As he drew near to the wood where he had left his wife, he heard a parrot on a tree calling out his name: "Mr. Vinegar, you foolish man, you blockhead, you simpleton; you went to the fair, and laid out all your money in buying a cow. Not content with that, you changed it for bag-pipes, on which you could not play, and which were not worth one-tenth of the money. You fool, you—you had no sooner got the bagpipes than you changed them for the gloves, which were not worth one-quarter of the money; and when you had got the gloves, you changed them for a poor miserable stick; and now for your forty guineas, cow, bagpipes, and gloves, you have nothing to show but that poor miserable stick, which you might have cut in any hedge." On this the bird laughed and laughed, and Mr. Vinegar, falling into a violent rage, threw the stick at its head. The stick lodged in the tree, and he returned to his wife without money, cow, bagpipes, gloves, or stick, and she instantly gave him such a sound cudgelling that she almost broke every bone in his skin.

Nix Nought Nothing

THERE once lived a king and a queen as many a one has been. They were long married and had no children; but at last a baby-boy came to the queen when the king was away in the far countries. The queen would not christen the boy till the king came back, and she said, " We will just call him *Nix Nought Nothing* until his father comes home." But it was long before he came home, and the boy had grown a fine, bonny laddie. At length the king was on his way back; but he had a big river to cross, and there was a whirlpool, and he could not get over the water. But a giant came up to him, and said : "I'll carry you over." But the king said : " What's your pay ? " " O give me Nix, Nought, Nothing, and I will carry you over the water on my back." The king had never heard that his son was called Nix Nought Nothing, and so he said : " O, I'll give you that and my thanks into the bargain." When the king got home again, he was very happy to see his wife again, and his young son. She told him that she had not given the child any name, but just Nix Nought Nothing, until he should come home again himself. The poor king was in a terrible case. He said : "What have I done ? I promised to give the giant who carried me over the river on his back, Nix Nought Nothing." The king and the queen were sad and sorry, but they said : "When the giant comes we will give him the hen-wife's boy ; he will never know the differ-ence." The next day the giant came to claim the king's promise, and he sent for the hen-wife's boy ; and the giant went away with the boy on his back. He travelled till he came to a big stone, and there he sat down to rest. He said :

"Hidge, Hodge, on my back, what time of day is that ?"

The poor little lad said : "It is the time that my mother, the hen-wife, takes up the eggs for the queen's breakfast."

Then the giant was very angry, and dashed the boy on the stone and killed him.

Back he went in a tower of a temper and this time they gave him the gardener's boy. He went off with him on his back till they got to the stone again when the giant sat down to rest. And he said :

" Hidge, Hodge, on my back, what time of day do you make that ? "

The gardener's boy said : " Sure it's the time that my mother takes up the vegetables for the queen's dinner."

Then the giant was as wild as could be, and killed him too.

Then the giant went back to the king's house in a terrible temper and said he would destroy them all if

they did not give him Nix Nought Nothing this time.
They had to do it; and when he came to the big
stone, the giant said: "What time of day is that?" Nix
Nought Nothing said: "It is the time that my father the
king will be sitting down to supper." The giant said:
"I've got the right one now;" and took Nix Nought
Nothing to his own house and brought him up till he was
a man.

The giant had a bonny daughter, and she and the lad
grew very fond of each other. The giant said one day
to Nix Nought Nothing: "I've work for you to-morrow.
There is a stable seven miles long and seven miles broad,
and it has not been cleaned for seven years, and you
must clean it to-morrow, or I will have you for my
supper."

The giant's daughter went out next morning with the
lad's breakfast, and found him in a terrible state, for
always as he cleaned out a bit, it just fell in again. The
giant's daughter said she would help him, and she cried
all the beasts in the field, and all the fowls of the air, and
in a minute they all came, and carried away everything
that was in the stable and made it all clean before the
giant came home. He said: "Shame on the wit that
helped you; but I have a worse job for you to-morrow."
Then he said to Nix Nought Nothing: "There's a lake
seven miles long, and seven miles deep, and seven miles
broad, and you must drain it to-morrow by nightfall, or
else I'll have you for my supper." Nix Nought Nothing
began early next morning and tried to lave the water
with his pail, but the lake was never getting any less,
and he didn't know what to do; but the giant's daughter

called on all the fish in the sea to come and drink the water, and very soon they drank it dry. When the giant saw the work done he was in a rage, and said : " I've a worse job for you to-morrow; there is a tree, seven miles high, and no branch on it, till you get to the top, and there is a nest with seven eggs in it, and you must bring down all the eggs without breaking one, or else I'll have

you for my supper." At first the giant's daughter did not know how to help Nix Nought Nothing ; but she cut off first her fingers and then her toes, and made steps of them, and he clomb the tree and got all the eggs safe till he came just to the bottom, and then one was broken. So they determined to run away together, and after the giant's daughter had gone back to her room, and got her magic flask they set out together as fast they could run. And they hadn't got but three fields away when they looked back and saw the giant walking along at full

speed after them. " Quick, quick," called out the giant's
daughter, "take my comb from my hair and throw it
down." Nix Nought Nothing took her comb from her
hair and threw it down, and out of every one of its prongs
there sprung up a fine thick briar in the way of the giant.
You may be sure it took him a long time to work his way
through the briar bush, and by the time he was well
through Nix Nought Nothing and his sweetheart had
run far far away from him. But he soon came along
after them and was just like to catch 'em up when the
giant's daughter called out to Nix Nought Nothing,
" Take my hair dagger and throw it down, quick, quick."
So Nix Nought Nothing threw down the hair dagger and
out of it grew as quick as lightning a thick hedge of
sharp razors placed criss cross. The giant had to tread
very cautiously to get through all this and meanwhile
they both ran hard, and on, and on, and on, till they were
nearly out of sight. But at last the giant was through,
and it wasn't long before he was like to catch them up.
But just as he was stretching out his hand to catch Nix
Nought Nothing his daughter took out her magic flask
and dashed it on the ground. And as it broke out of it
welled a big, big wave that grew, and that grew, till it
reached the giant's waist and then his neck, and when it
got to his head, he was drowned dead, and dead, and
dead indeed.

But Nix Nought Nothing fled on till where do you
think they came to? Why, to near the castle of Nix
Nought Nothing's father and mother. But the giant's
daughter was so weary that she couldn't move a step
further. So Nix Nought Nothing told her to wait there

while he went and found out a lodging for the night.
And he went on towards the lights of the castle, and
on the way he came to the cottage of the hen-wife
whose boy, you'll remember, had been killed by the giant.
Now she knew Nix Nought Nothing in a moment, and
hated him because he was the cause of her son's death.
So when he asked his way to the castle she put a spell
upon him, and when he got to the castle, no sooner was
he let in than he fell down dead asleep upon a bench in
the hall.   The king and queen tried all they could do to
wake him up, but all in vain.   So the king promised that
if any maiden could wake him she should marry him.
Meanwhile the giant's daughter was waiting and waiting
for him to come back.   And she went up into a tree to
watch for him.   The gardener's daughter, going to draw
water in the well, saw the shadow of the lady in the water
and thought it was herself, and said : "If I'm so bonny,
if I'm so brave, why do you send me to draw water ? "
So she threw down her pail and went to see if she could
wed the sleeping stranger.   And she went to the hen-
wife, who taught her an unspelling charm which would
keep Nix Nought Nothing awake as long as the
gardener's daughter liked.   So she went up to the castle
and sang her charm and Nix Nought Nothing was
wakened for a while and they promised to wed him to the
gardener's daughter.   Meanwhile the gardener went
down to draw water from the well and saw the shadow of
the lady in the water.   So he looked up and found her,
and he brought the lady from the tree, and led her into
his house.   And he told her that a stranger was to marry
his daughter, and took her up to the castle and showed

her the man : and it was Nix Nought Nothing asleep in a chair. And she saw him, and cried to him : "Waken, waken, and speak to me!" But he would not waken, and soon she cried :

> "I cleaned the stable, I laved the lake, and I clomb the tree,
> And all for the love of thee,
> And thou wilt not waken and speak to me."

The king and the queen heard this, and came to the bonny young lady, and she said :

"I cannot get Nix Nought Nothing to speak to me for all that I can do."

Then were they greatly astonished when she spoke of Nix Nought Nothing, and asked where he was, and she said : "He that sits there in the chair." Then they ran to him and kissed him and called him their own dear son ; so they called for the gardener's daughter and made her sing her charm, and he wakened, and told them all that the giant's daughter had done for him, and of all her kindness. Then they took her in their arms and kissed her, and said she should now be their daughter, for their son should marry her. But as for the hen-wife, she was put to death. And they lived happy all their days.

Jack Hannaford

THERE was an old soldier who had been long in the wars—so long, that he was quite out-at-elbows, and he did not know where to go to find a living. So he walked up moors, down glens, till at last he came to a farm, from which the good man had gone away to market. The wife of the farmer was a very foolish woman, who had been a widow when he married her; the farmer was foolish enough, too, and it is hard to say which of the two was the more foolish. When you've heard my tale you may decide.

Now before the farmer goes to market says he to his wife: "Here is ten pounds all in gold, take care of it till I come home." If the man had not been a fool he would never have given the money to his wife to keep. Well, off he went in his cart to market, and the wife said to herself: "I will keep the ten pounds quite safe from thieves;" so she tied it up in a rag, and she put the rag up the parlour chimney.

"There," said she, "no thieves will ever find it now, that is quite sure."

Jack Hannaford, the old soldier, came and rapped at the door.

"Who is there?" asked the wife.

"Jack Hannaford."

"Where do you come from?"

"Paradise."

"Lord a' mercy! and maybe you've seen my old man there," alluding to her former husband.

"Yes, I have."

"And how was he a-doing?" asked the goody.

"But middling; he cobbles old shoes, and he has nothing but cabbage for victuals."

"Deary me!" exclaimed the woman. "Didn't he send a message to me?"

"Yes, he did," replied Jack Hannaford. "He said that he was out of leather, and his pockets were empty, so you were to send him a few shillings to buy a fresh stock of leather."

"He shall have them, bless his poor soul!" And away went the wife to the parlour chimney, and she pulled the rag with the ten pounds in it from the chimney, and she gave the whole sum to the soldier, telling him that her old man was to use as much as he wanted, and to send back the rest.

It was not long that Jack waited after receiving the money; he went off as fast as he could walk.

Presently the farmer came home and asked for his money. The wife told him that she had sent it by a soldier to her former husband in Paradise, to buy him leather for cobbling the shoes of the saints and angels of Heaven. The farmer was very angry, and he swore that he had never met with such a fool as his wife. But the wife said that her husband was a greater fool for letting her have the money.

There was no time to waste words; so the farmer mounted his horse and rode off after Jack Hanna-ford. The old soldier heard the horse's hoofs clattering on the road behind him, so he knew it must be the farmer pursuing him. He lay down on the ground, and shading his eyes with one hand, looked up into the sky, and pointed heavenwards with the other hand.

"What are you about there?" asked the farmer, pulling up.

"Lord save you!" exclaimed Jack: "I've seen a rare sight."

"What was that?"

"A man going straight up into the sky, as if he were walking on a road."

"Can you see him still?"

"Yes, I can."

"Where?"

"Get off your horse and lie down."

"If you will hold the horse."

Jack did so readily.

"I cannot see him," said the farmer.

"Shade your eyes with your hand, and you'll soon see a man flying away from you."

Sure enough he did so, for Jack leaped on the horse, and rode away with it. The farmer walked home without his horse.

"You are a bigger fool than I am," said the wife;
"for I did only one foolish thing, and you have done
two."

Binnorie

ONCE upon a time there were two king's daughters lived in a bower near the bonny milldams of Binnorie. And Sir William came wooing the eldest and won her love, and plighted troth with glove and with ring. But after a time he looked upon the youngest, with her cherry cheeks and golden hair, and his love went out to her till he cared no longer for the eldest one. So she hated her sister for taking away Sir William's love, and day by day her hate grew and grew and she plotted and she planned how to get rid of her.

So one fine morning, fair and clear, she said to her sister, " Let us go and see our father's boats come in at the bonny mill-stream of Binnorie." So they went there hand in hand. And when they came to the river's bank the youngest got upon a stone to watch for the beaching of the boats. And her sister, coming behind her, caught her round the waist and dashed her into the rushing mill-stream of Binnorie.

BINNORIE.

"O sister, sister, reach me your hand!" she cried, as she floated away, "and you shall have half of all I've got or shall get."

"No, sister, I'll reach you no hand of mine, for I am the heir to all your land. Shame on me if I touch her hand that has come 'twixt me and my own heart's love."

"O sister, O sister, then reach me your glove!" she cried, as she floated further away, "and you shall have your William again."

"Sink on," cried the cruel princess, "no hand or glove of mine you'll touch. Sweet William will be all mine when you are sunk beneath the bonny mill-stream of Binnorie." And she turned and went home to the king's castle.

And the princess floated down the mill-stream, sometimes swimming and sometimes sinking, till she came near the mill. Now the miller's daughter was cooking that day, and needed water for her cooking. And as she went to draw it from the stream, she saw something floating towards the mill-dam, and she called out, "Father! father! draw your dam. There's something white—a merrymaid or a milk-white swan—coming down the stream." So the miller hastened to the dam and stopped the heavy cruel mill-wheels. And then they took out the princess and laid her on the bank.

Fair and beautiful she looked as she lay there. In her golden hair were pearls and precious stones; you could not see her waist for her golden girdle, and the golden fringe of her white dress came down over her lily feet. But she was drowned, drowned!

And as she lay there in her beauty a famous harper passed by the mill-dam of Binnorie, and saw her sweet pale face. And though he travelled on far away he never forgot that face, and after many days he came back to the bonny mill-stream of Binnorie. But then all he could find of her where they had put her to rest were her bones and her golden hair. So he made a harp out of her breast-bone and her hair, and travelled on up the hill from the mill-dam of Binnorie, till he came to the castle of the king her father.

That night they were all gathered in the castle hall to hear the great harper—king and queen, their daughter and son, Sir William and all their Court. And first the harper sang to his old harp, making them joy and be glad, or sorrow and weep just as he liked. But while he sang he put the harp he had made that day on a stone in the hall. And presently it began to sing by itself, low and clear, and the harper stopped and all were hushed.

And this was what the harp sung:

> " O yonder sits my father, the king,
>   Binnorie, O Binnorie;
>   And yonder sits my mother, the queen;
>   By the bonny mill-dams o' Binnorie.
>
> "And yonder stands my brother Hugh,
>   Binnorie, O Binnorie;
>   And by him, my William, false and true;
>   By the bonny mill-dams o' Binnorie."

Then they all wondered, and the harper told them how he had seen the princess lying drowned on the bank near

the bonny mill-dams o' Binnorie, and how he had afterwards made this harp out of her hair and breast-bone.
Just then the harp began singing again, and this was what
it sang out loud and clear:

> "And there sits my sister who drownèd me
> By the bonny mill-dams o' Binnorie."

And the harp snapped and broke, and never sang
more.

Mouse and Mouser

THE Mouse went to visit the Cat, and found her sitting behind the hall door, spinning.

MOUSE.

What are you doing, my lady, my lady,
What are you doing, my lady?

CAT (*sharply*).

I'm spinning old breeches, good body, good body,
I'm spinning old breeches, good body.

Mouse and Mouser

MOUSE.

Long may you wear them, my lady, my lady,
Long may you wear them, my lady.

CAT (*gruffly*).

I'll wear 'em and tear 'em, good body, good body,
I'll wear 'em and tear 'em, good body.

MOUSE.

I was sweeping my room, my lady, my lady,
I was sweeping my room, my lady.

CAT.

The cleaner you'd be, good body, good body,
The cleaner you'd be, good body.

MOUSE.

I found a silver sixpence, my lady, my lady,
I found a silver sixpence, my lady.

CAT.

The richer you were, good body, good body,
The richer you were, good body.

MOUSE.

I went to the market, my lady my lady,
I went to the market, my lady.

CAT.

The further you went, good body, good body,
The further you went, good body.

MOUSE.

I bought me a pudding, my lady, my lady,
I bought me a pudding, my lady.

CAT (*snarling*).

The more meat you had, good body, good body,
The more meat you had, good body.

MOUSE.

I put it in the window to cool, my lady,
I put it in the window to cool.

CAT (*sharply*).

The faster you'd eat it, good body, good body,
The faster you'd eat it, good body.

MOUSE (*timidly*).

The cat came and ate it, my lady, my lady,
The cat came and ate it, my lady.

CAT (*pouncingly*).

And Il'l eat you, good body, good body,
And I'll eat you, good body.

(*Springs upon the mouse and kills it.*)

Cap o' Rushes

WELL, there was once a very rich gentleman, and he'd three daughters, and he thought he'd see how fond they were of him. So he says to the first, "How much do you love me, my dear?"

"Why," says she, "as I love my life."

"That's good," says he.

So he says to the second, " How much do *you* love me, my dear ?"

"Why," says she, "better nor all the world."

"That's good," says he.

So he says to the third, " How much do *you* love me, my dear ? "

" Why, I love you as fresh meat loves salt," says she.

Well, but he was angry. " You don't love me at all," says he, "and in my house you stay no more." So he drove her out there and then, and shut the door in her face.

Well, she went away on and on till she came to a fen, and there she gathered a lot of rushes and made them into a kind of a sort of a cloak with a hood, to cover her from head to foot, and to hide her fine clothes. And then she went on and on till she came to a great house.

"Do you want a maid ? " says she.

"No, we don't," said they.

"I haven't nowhere to go," says she ; "and I ask no wages, and do any sort of work," says she.

"Well," said they, " if you like to wash the pots and scrape the saucepans you may stay," said they.

So she stayed there and washed the pots and scraped the saucepans and did all the dirty work. And because she gave no name they called her "Cap o' Rushes."

Well, one day there was to be a great dance a little way off, and the servants were allowed to go and look on at the grand people. Cap o' Rushes said she was too tired to go, so she stayed at home.

But when they were gone she offed with her cap o'

rushes, and cleaned herself, and went to the dance. And no one there was so finely dressed as she.

Well, who should be there but her master's son, and what should he do but fall in love with her the minute he set eyes on her. He wouldn't dance with any one else.

But before the dance was done Cap o' Rushes slipt off, and away she went home. And when the other maids came back she was pretending to be asleep with her cap o' rushes on.

Well, next morning they said to her, "You did miss a sight, Cap o' Rushes!"

"What was that?" says she.

"Why, the beautifullest lady you ever see, dressed right gay and ga'. The young master, he never took his eyes off her."

"Well, I should have liked to have seen her," says Cap o' Rushes.

"Well, there's to be another dance this evening, and perhaps she'll be there."

But, come the evening, Cap o' Rushes said she was too tired to go with them. Howsoever, when they were gone she offed with her cap o' rushes and cleaned herself, and away she went to the dance.

The master's son had been reckoning on seeing her, and he danced with no one else, and never took his eyes off her. But, before the dance was over, she slipt off, and home she went, and when the maids came back she pretended to be asleep with her cap o rushes on.

Next day they said to her again, "Well, Cap o' Rushes, you should ha' been there to see the lady. There she was again, gay and ga', and the young master he never took his eyes off her."

"Well, there," says she, " I should ha' liked to ha' seen her."

"Well," says they, " there's a dance again this evening, and you must go with us, for she's sure to be there."

Well, come this evening, Cap o' Rushes said she was too tired to go, and do what they would she stayed at home. But when they were gone she offed with her cap o' rushes and cleaned herself, and away she went to the dance.

The master's son was rarely glad when he saw her. He danced with none but her and never took his eyes off her. When she wouldn't tell him her name, nor where she came from, he gave her a ring and told her if he didn't see her again he should die.

Well, before the dance was over, off she slipped, and home she went, and when the maids came home she was pretending to be asleep with her cap o' rushes on.

Well, next day they says to her, "There, Cap o' Rushes, you didn't come last night, and now you won't see the lady, for there's no more dances."

" Well I should have rarely liked to have seen her," says she.

The master's son he tried every way to find out where the lady was gone, but go where he might, and ask whom he might, he never heard anything about her. And he got worse and worse for the love of her till he had to keep his bed.

" Make some gruel for the young master," they said to the cook. " He's dying for the love of the lady." The cook she set about making it when Cap o' Rushes came in.

"What are you a-doing of?" says she.

"I'm going to make some gruel for the young master," says the cook, "for he's dying for love of the lady."

"Let me make it," says Cap o' Rushes.

Well, the cook wouldn't at first, but at last she said yes, and Cap o' Rushes made the gruel. And when she had made it she slipped the ring into it on the sly before the cook took it upstairs.

The young man he drank it and then he saw the ring at the bottom.

"Send for the cook," says he.

So up she comes.

"Who made this gruel here?" says he.

"I did," says the cook, for she was frightened.

And he looked at her.

"No, you didn't," says he. "Say who did it, and you shan't be harmed."

"Well, then, 'twas Cap o' Rushes," says she.

"Send Cap o' Rushes here," says he.

So Cap o' Rushes came.

"Did you make my gruel?" says he.

"Yes, I did," says she.

"Where did you get this ring?" says he.

"From him that gave it me," says she.

"Who are you, then?" says the young man.

"I'll show you," says she. And she offed with her cap o' rushes, and there she was in her beautiful clothes.

Well, the master's son he got well very soon, and they were to be married in a little time. It was to be a very

grand wedding, and every one was asked far and near.
And Cap o' Rushes' father was asked.   But she never
told anybody who she was.

But before the wedding she went to the cook, and says
she :

"I want you to dress every dish without a mite o'
salt."

"That'll be rare nasty," says the cook.

"That doesn't signify," says she.

"Very well," says the cook.

Well, the wedding-day came, and they were married.
And after they were married all the company sat down to
the dinner.   When they began to eat the meat, it was
so tasteless they couldn't eat it.   But Cap o' Rushes'
father tried first one dish and then another, and then he
burst out crying.

"What is the matter?" said the master's son to him.

"Oh!" says he, "I had a daughter.   And I asked her
how much she loved me.   And she said 'As much as
fresh meat loves salt.'   And I turned her from my door,
for I thought she didn't love me.   And now I see she
loved me best of all.   And she may be dead for aught I
know."

"No, father, here she is!" says Cap o' Rushes.   And
she goes up to him and puts her arms round him.

And so they were all happy ever after.

Teeny-Tiny

ONCE upon a time there was a teeny-tiny woman lived in a teeny-tiny house in a teeny-tiny village. Now, one day this teeny-tiny woman put on her teeny-tiny bonnet, and went out of her teeny-tiny house to take a teeny-tiny walk. And when this teeny-tiny woman had gone a teeny-tiny way she came to a teeny-tiny gate; so the teeny-tiny woman opened the teeny-tiny gate, and went into a teeny-tiny churchyard. And when this teeny-tiny woman had got into the teeny-tiny churchyard, she saw a teeny-tiny bone on a teeny-tiny grave, and the teeny-tiny woman said to her teeny-tiny self, " This teeny-tiny bone will make me some teeny-tiny soup for my teeny-tiny supper." So the teeny-tiny woman put the teeny-tiny bone into her teeny-tiny pocket, and went home to her teeny-tiny house.

Now when the teeny-tiny woman got home to her teeny-tiny house she was a teeny-tiny bit tired; so she went up her teeny-tiny stairs to her teeny-tiny bed, and put the teeny-tiny bone into a teeny-tiny cupboard. And when this teeny-tiny woman had been to sleep a teeny-tiny time, she was awakened by a teeny-tiny voice from the teeny-tiny cupboard, which said :

"Give me my bone !"

And this teeny-tiny woman was a teeny-tiny frightened, so she hid her teeny-tiny head under the teeny-tiny clothes and went to sleep again. And when she had been to sleep again a teeny-tiny time, the teeny-tiny voice again cried out from the teeny-tiny cupboard a teeny-tiny louder,

"Give me my bone !"

This made the teeny-tiny woman a teeny-tiny more frightened, so she hid her teeny-tiny head a teeny-tiny further under the teeny-tiny clothes. And when the teeny-tiny woman had been to sleep again a teeny-tiny time, the teeny-tiny voice from the teeny-tiny cupboard said again a teeny-tiny louder,

"Give me my bone !"

And this teeny-tiny woman was a teeny-tiny bit more frightened, but she put her teeny-tiny head out of the teeny-tiny clothes, and said in her loudest teeny-tiny voice, "TAKE IT !"

Jack and the Beanstalk

THERE was once upon a time a poor widow who had an only son named Jack, and a cow named Milky-white. And all they had to live on was the milk the cow gave every morning which they carried to the market and sold. But one morning Milky-white gave no milk and they didn't know what to do.

"What shall we do, what shall **we** do?" said the widow, wringing her hands.

"Cheer up, mother, I'll go and get work somewhere," said Jack.

"We've tried that before, and nobody would take you," said his mother; "we must sell Milky-white and with the money start shop, or something."

"All right, mother," says Jack; "it's market-day to-day, and I'll soon sell Milky-white, and then we'll see what we can do."

So he took the cow's halter in his hand, and off he started. He hadn't gone far when he met a funny-looking old man who said to him: "Good morning, Jack."

"Good morning to you," said Jack, and wondered how he knew his name.

"Well, Jack, and where are you off to?" said the man.

"I'm going to market to sell our cow here."

"Oh, you look the proper sort of chap to sell cows," said the man; "I wonder if you know how many beans make five."

"Two in each hand and one in your mouth," says Jack, as sharp as a needle.

"Right you are," says the man, "and here they are, the very beans themselves," he went on, pulling out of his pocket a number of strange-looking beans. "As you are so sharp," says he, "I don't mind doing a swop with you—your cow for these beans."

"Go along," says Jack; "wouldn't you like it?"

"Ah! you don't know what these beans are," said the man; "if you plant them over-night, by morning they grow right up to the sky."

"Really?" says Jack; "you don't say so."

"Yes, that is so, and if it doesn't turn out to be true you can have your cow back."

"Right," says Jack, and hands him over Milky-white's halter and pockets the beans.

Back goes Jack home, and as he hadn't gone very far it wasn't dusk by the time he got to his door.

"Back already, Jack?" said his mother; "I see you haven't got Milky-white, so you've sold her.   How much did you get for her?"

"You'll never guess, mother," says Jack.

"No, you don't say so.   Good boy!   Five pounds, ten, fifteen, no, it can't be twenty."

"I told you you couldn't guess, what do you say to these beans; they're magical, plant them over-night and——"

"What!" says Jack's mother, "have you been such a fool, such a dolt, such an idiot, as to give away my Milky-white, the best milker in the parish, and prime beef to boot, for a set of paltry beans.   Take that! Take that! Take that!   And as for your precious beans here they go out of the window.   And now off with you to bed.   Not a sup shall you drink, and not a bit shall you swallow this very night."

So Jack went upstairs to his little room in the attic, and sad and sorry he was, to be sure, as much for his mother's sake, as for the loss of his supper.

At last he dropped off to sleep.

When he woke up, the room looked so funny.   The sun was shining into part of it, and yet all the rest was quite dark and shady.   So Jack jumped up and dressed himself and went to the window.   And what do you think he saw?   why, the beans his mother had thrown out of the window into the garden, had sprung up into a big beanstalk which went up and up and up till it reached the sky.   So the man spoke truth after all.

The beanstalk grew up quite close past Jack's window, so all he had to do was to open it and give a jump on to the beanstalk which ran up just like a big ladder. So Jack climbed, and he climbed and he climbed and he climbed and he climbed and he climbed and he climbed till at last he reached the sky. And when he got there he found a long broad road going as straight as a dart. So he walked along and he walked along and he walked along till he came to a great big tall house, and on the doorstep there was a great big tall woman.

"Good morning, mum," says Jack, quite polite-like. "Could you be so kind as to give me some breakfast?" For he hadn't had anything to eat, you know, the night before and was as hungry as a hunter.

"It's breakfast you want, is it?" says the great big tall woman, "it's breakfast you'll be if you don't move off from here. My man is an ogre and there's nothing he likes better than boys broiled on toast. You'd better be moving on or he'll soon be coming."

"Oh! please mum, do give me something to eat, mum. I've had nothing to eat since yesterday morning, really and truly, mum," says Jack, "I may as well be broiled as die of hunger."

Well, the ogre's wife was not half so bad after all. So she took Jack into the kitchen, and gave him a junk of bread and cheese and a jug of milk. But Jack hadn't half finished these when thump! thump! thump! the whole house began to tremble with the noise of some one coming.

"Goodness gracious me! It's my old man," said the ogre's wife, " what on earth shall I do? Come along quick and jump in here." And she bundled Jack into the oven just as the ogre came in.

He was a big one, to be sure. At his belt he had three calves strung up by the heels, and he unhooked them and threw them down on the table and said : " Here, wife, broil me a couple of these for breakfast. Ah! what's this I smell ?

> Fee-fi-fo-fum,
> I smell the blood of an Englishman,
> Be he alive, or be he dead
> I'll have his bones to grind my bread."

" Nonsense, dear," said his wife, " you're dreaming. Or perhaps you smell the scraps of that little boy you liked so much for yesterday's dinner. Here, you go and have a wash and tidy up, and by the time you come back your breakfast'll be ready for you."

So off the ogre went, and Jack was just going to jump out of the oven and run away when the woman told him not. " Wait till he's asleep," says she ; " he always has a doze after breakfast."

Well, the ogre had his breakfast, and after that he goes to a big chest and takes out of it a couple of bags of gold, and down he sits and counts till at last his head began to nod and he began to snore till the whole house shook again.

Then Jack crept out on tiptoe from his oven, and as he was passing the ogre he took one of the bags of gold under his arm, and off he pelters till he came to the bean-stalk, and then he threw down the bag of gold, which of course fell in to his mother's garden, and then he climbed down and climbed down till at last he got home and told his mother and showed her the gold and said : " Well, mother, wasn't I right about the beans. They are really magical, you see."

So they lived on the bag of gold for some time, but at last they came to the end of it, and Jack made up his mind to try his luck once more up at the top of the beanstalk. So one fine morning he rose up early, and got on to the beanstalk, and he climbed and he climbed and he climbed and he climbed and he climbed and he climbed till at last he came out on to the road again and up to the great big tall house he had been to before. There, sure enough, was the great big tall woman a-standing on the door-step.

" Good morning, mum," says Jack, as bold as brass, " could you be so good as to give me something to eat ? "

" Go away, my bôy," said the big tall woman, " or else my man will eat you up for breakfast. But aren't you the youngster who came here once before ? Do you know, that very day, my man missed one of his bags of gold."

" That's strange, mum," says Jack, " I dare say I could tell you something about that, but I'm so hungry I can't speak till I've had something to eat."

Well the big tall woman was so curious that she took him in and gave him something to eat. But he had scarcely begun munching it as slowly as he could when thump ! thump ! thump ! they heard the giant's footstep, and his wife hid Jack away in the oven.

All happened as it did before. In came the ogre as he did before, said : " Fee-fi-fo-fum," and had his breakfast off three broiled oxen. Then he said : " Wife, bring me the hen that lays the golden eggs." So she brought it, and the ogre said : " Lay," and it laid an egg all of gold. And then the ogre began to nod his head, and to snore till the house shook.

Then Jack crept out of the oven on tiptoe and caught hold of the golden hen, and was off before you could say " Jack Robinson." But this time the hen gave a cackle which woke the ogre, and just as Jack got out of the house he heard him calling : " Wife, wife, what have you done with my golden hen ? "

And the wife said : " Why, my dear ? "

But that was all Jack heard, for he rushed off to the beanstalk and climbed down like a house on fire. And when he got home he showed his mother the wonderful hen and said " Lay," to it ; and it laid a golden egg every time he said " Lay."

Well, Jack was not content, and it wasn't very long before he determined to have another try at his luck up there at the top of the beanstalk. So one fine morning, he rose up early, and got on to the beanstalk, and he climbed and he climbed and he climbed and he climbed till he got to the top. But this time he knew better than to go straight to the ogre's house. And when he got near it he waited behind a bush till he saw the ogre's wife come out with a pail to get some water, and then he crept into the house and got into the copper. He hadn't been there long when he heard thump ! thump ! thump ! as before, and in come the ogre and his wife.

" Fee-fi-fo-fum, I smell the blood of an Englishman,' cried out the ogre ; " I smell him, wife, I smell him."

"Do you, my dearie?" says the ogre's wife. "Then if it's that little rogue that stole your gold and the hen that laid the golden eggs he's sure to have got into the oven." And they both rushed to the oven. But Jack wasn't there, luckily, and the ogre's wife said: "There you are again with your fee-fi-fo-fum. Why of course it's the boy you caught last night that I've just broiled for your breakfast. How forgetful I am, and how careless you are not to know the difference between live and dead after all these years."

So the ogre sat down to the breakfast and ate it, but every now and then he would mutter: "Well, I could have sworn——" and he'd get up and search the larder and the cupboards, and everything, only luckily he didn't think of the copper.

After breakfast was over, the ogre called out: "Wife, wife, bring me my golden harp." So she brought it and put it on the table before him. Then he said: "Sing!" and the golden harp sang most beautifully. And it went on singing till the ogre fell asleep, and commenced to snore like thunder.

Then Jack lifted up the copper-lid very quietly and got down like a mouse and crept on hands and knees till he came to the table when up he crawled, caught hold of the golden harp and dashed with it towards the door. But the harp called out quite loud: "Master! Master!" and the ogre woke up just in time to see Jack running off with his harp.

Jack ran as fast as he could, and the ogre came rushing after, and would soon have caught him only Jack had a start and dodged him a bit and knew where he was going.

When he got to the beanstalk the ogre was not more than twenty yards away when suddenly he saw Jack disappear like, and when he came to the end of the road he saw Jack underneath climbing down for dear life. Well, the ogre didn't like trusting himself to such a ladder, and he stood and waited, so Jack got another start. But just then the harp cried out : " Master ! master ! " and the ogre swung himself down on to the beanstalk which shook with his weight. Down climbs Jack, and after him climbed the ogre. By this time Jack had climbed down and climbed down and climbed down till he was very nearly home. So he called out : " Mother ! mother ! bring me an axe, bring me an axe." And his mother came rushing out with the axe in her hand, but when she came to the beanstalk she stood stock still with fright for there she saw the ogre with his legs just through the clouds.

But Jack jumped down and got hold of the axe and gave a chop at the beanstalk which cut it half in two. The ogre felt the beanstalk shake and quiver so he stopped to see what was the matter. Then Jack gave another chop with the axe, and the beanstalk was cut in two and began to topple over. Then the ogre fell down and broke his crown, and the beanstalk came toppling after.

Then Jack showed his mother his golden harp, and what with showing that and selling the golden eggs, Jack and his mother became very rich, and he married a great princess, and they lived happy ever after.

The Story of the Three
Little Pigs

Once upon a time when pigs spoke rhyme
And monkeys chewed tobacco,
And hens took snuff to make them tough,
And ducks went quack, quack, quack, O !

THERE was an old sow with three little pigs,
and as she had not enough to keep them, she
sent them out to seek their fortune. The first
that went off met a man with a bundle of straw, and said
to him :

"Please, man, give me that straw to build me a
house."

Which the man did, and the little pig built a house with it. Presently came along a wolf, and knocked at the door, and said :

" Little pig, little pig, let me come in."

To which the pig answered :

" No, no, by the hair of my chiny chin chin."

The wolf then answered to that :

" Then I'll huff, and I'll puff, and I'll blow your house in."

So he huffed, and he puffed, and he blew his house in, and ate up the little pig.

The second little pig met a man with a bundle of furze, and said :

" Please, man, give me that furze to build a house."

Which the man did, and the pig built his house. Then along came the wolf, and said :

" Little pig, little pig, let me come in."

" No, no, by the hair of my chiny chin chin."

" Then I'll puff, and I'll huff, and I'll blow your house in."

So he huffed, and he puffed, and he puffed, and he huffed, and at last he blew the house down, and he ate up the little pig.

The third little pig met a man with a load of bricks, and said :

" Please, man, give me those bricks to build a house with."

So the man gave him the bricks, and he built his house with them.   So the wolf came, as he did to the other little pigs, and said :

" Little pig, little pig, let me come in."

"No, no, by the hair of my chiny chin chin."

"Then I'll huff, and I'll puff, and I'll blow your house in."

Well, he huffed, and he puffed, and he huffed and he puffed, and he puffed and huffed; but he could *not* get the house down. When he found that he could not, with all his huffing and puffing, blow the house down, he said:

"Little pig, I know where there is a nice field of turnips."

"Where?" said the little pig.

"Oh, in Mr. Smith's Home-field, and if you will be ready to-morrow morning I will call for you, and we will go together, and get some for dinner."

"Very well," said the little pig, "I will be ready. What time do you mean to go?"

"Oh, at six o'clock."

Well, the little pig got up at five, and got the turnips before the wolf came (which he did about six) and who said:

"Little pig, are you ready?"

The little pig said: "Ready! I have been and come back again, and got a nice potful for dinner."

The wolf felt very angry at this, but thought that he would be up to the little pig somehow or other, so he said:

"Little pig, I know where there is a nice apple-tree."

"Where?" said the pig.

"Down at Merry-garden," replied the wolf, "and if you will not deceive me I will come for you, at five o'clock to-morrow and get some apples."

Well, the little pig bustled up the next morning at four o'clock, and went off for the apples, hoping to get back before the wolf came ; but he had further to go, and had to climb the tree, so that just as he was coming down from it, he saw the wolf coming, which, as you may suppose, frightened him very much. When the wolf came up he said :

"Little pig, what! are you here before me ? Are they nice apples ? "

"Yes, very," said the little pig. "I will throw you down one."

And he threw it so far, that, while the wolf was gone to pick it up, the little pig jumped down and ran home. The next day the wolf came again, and said to the little pig :

"Little pig, there is a fair at Shanklin this afternoon, will you go ? "

"Oh yes," said the pig, "I will go ; what time shall you be ready ? "

"At three," said the wolf. So the little pig went off before the time as usual, and got to the fair, and bought a butter-churn, which he was going home with, when he saw the wolf coming. Then he could not tell what to do. So he got into the churn to hide, and by so doing turned it round, and it rolled down the hill with the pig in it, which frightened the wolf so much, that he ran home without going to the fair. He went to the little pig's house, and told him how frightened he had been by a great round thing which came down the hill past him. Then the little pig said :

"Hah, I frightened you, then. I had been to the fair

and bought a butter-churn, and when I saw you, I got into it, and rolled down the hill."

Then the wolf was very angry indeed, and declared he *would* eat up the little pig, and that he would get down the chimney after him. When the little pig saw what he was about, he hung on the pot full of water, and made up a blazing fire, and, just as the wolf was coming down, took off the cover, and in fell the wolf ; so the little pig put on the cover again in an instant, boiled him up, and ate him for supper, and lived happy ever afterwards.

The Master and his Pupil

THERE was once a very learned man in the north-country who knew all the languages under the sun, and who was acquainted with all the mysteries of creation. He had one big book bound in black calf and clasped with iron, and with iron corners, and chained to a table which was made fast to the floor ; and when he read out of this book, he unlocked it with an iron key, and none but he read from it, for it contained all the secrets of the spiritual world. It told how many angels there were in heaven, and how they marched in their ranks, and sang in their quires, and what were their several functions, and what was the name of each great angel of might. And it told of the demons, how many of them there were, and what were their several powers, and their labours, and their names, and how they might be summoned, and how tasks might be imposed on them, and how they might be chained to be as slaves to man.

Now the master had a pupil who was but a foolish lad, and he acted as servant to the great master, but never was he suffered to look into the black book, hardly to enter the private room.

One day the master was out, and then the lad, as curious as could be, hurried to the chamber where his master kept his wondrous apparatus for changing copper into gold, and lead into silver, and where was his mirror in which he could see all that was passing in the world, and where was the shell which when held to the ear whispered all the words that were being spoken by any one the master desired to know about. The lad tried in vain with the crucibles to turn copper and lead into gold and silver—he looked long and vainly into the mirror; smoke and clouds passed over it, but he saw nothing plain, and the shell to his ear produced only indistinct murmurings, like the breaking of distant seas on an unknown shore. "I can do nothing," he said ; "as I don't know the right words to utter, and they are locked up in yon book."

He looked round, and, see! the book was unfastened ; the master had forgotten to lock it before he went out. The boy rushed to it, and unclosed the volume. It was written with red and black ink, and much of it he could not understand; but he put his finger on a line and spelled it through.

At once the room was darkened, and the house trembled; a clap of thunder rolled through the passage and the old room, and there stood before him a horrible, horrible form, breathing fire, and with eyes like burning lamps. It was the demon Beelzebub, whom he had called up to serve him.

"Set me a task!" said he, with a voice like the roaring of an iron furnace.

The boy only trembled, and his hair stood up.

"Set me a task, or I shall strangle thee!"

But the lad could not speak. Then the evil spirit stepped towards him, and putting forth his hands touched his throat. The fingers burned his flesh. "Set me a task!"

"Water yon flower," cried the boy in despair, pointing to a geranium which stood in a pot on the floor.

Instantly the spirit left the room, but in another instant he returned with a barrel on his back, and poured its contents over the flower ; and again and again he went and came, and poured more and more water, till the floor of the room was ankle-deep.

"Enough, enough!" gasped the lad; but the demon heeded him not ; the lad didn't know the words by which to send him away, and still he fetched water.

It rose to the boy's knees and still more water was

poured.   It mounted to his waist, and Beelzebub still kept on bringing barrels full.   It rose to his armpits, and he scrambled to the table-top.   And now the water in the room stood up to the window and washed against the glass, and swirled around his feet on the table.   It still rose; it reached his breast.   In vain he cried ; the evil spirit would not be dismissed, and to this day he would have been pouring water, and would have drowned all Yorkshire. But the master remembered on his journey that he had not locked his book, and therefore returned, and at the moment when the water was bubbling about the pupil's chin, rushed into the room and spoke the words which cast Beelzebub back into his fiery home.

Titty Mouse and Tatty Mouse

TITTY MOUSE and Tatty Mouse both lived in a house,
    Titty Mouse went a leasing and Tatty Mouse went a leasing,
  So they both went a leasing.
Titty Mouse leased an ear of corn, and Tatty Mouse leased an ear of corn,
  So they both leased an ear of corn.
Titty Mouse made a pudding, and Tatty Mouse made a pudding,
  So they both made a pudding.
And Tatty Mouse put her pudding into the pot to boil,

But when Titty went to put hers in, the pot tumbled over, and scalded her to death.

Then Tatty sat down and wept; then a three-legged stool said: "Tatty, why do you weep?" "Titty's dead," said Tatty, and so I weep;" "then," said the stool, "I'll hop," so the stool hopped.

Then a broom in the corner of the room said, "Stool, why do you hop?" "Oh!" said the stool, "Titty's dead, and Tatty weeps, and so I hop;"

So the Stool hopped. "then," said the broom, "I'll sweep," so the broom began to sweep.

"Then," said the door, "Broom, why do you sweep?" "Oh!" said the broom, "Titty's dead, and Tatty weeps, and the stool hops, and so I sweep;" "then," said the door, "I'll jar," so the door jarred.

"Then," said the window, "Door, why do you jar?" "Oh!" said the door, "Titty's dead, and Tatty weeps, and the stool hops, and the broom sweeps, and so I jar."

"Then," said the window, "I'll creak," so the window creaked. Now there was an old form outside the house, and when the window creaked, the form said: "Window, why do you creak?" "Oh!" said the window, "Titty's dead, and Tatty weeps, and the stool hops, and the broom sweeps, the door jars, and so I creak."

"Then," said the old form, "I'll run round the house;" then the old form ran round the house. Now there was a fine large walnut-tree growing by the cottage, and the tree said to the form: "Form, why do you run round the house?" "Oh!" said the form, "Titty's dead, and

Tatty weeps, and the stool hops, and the broom sweeps, the door jars, and the window creaks, and so I run round the house."

" So I run round the house."

" Then," said the walnut-tree, " I'll shed my leaves," so the walnut-tree shed all its beautiful green leaves. Now there was a little bird perched on one of the boughs of the tree, and when all the leaves fell, it said : " Walnut-tree, why do you shed your leaves ? " " Oh ! " said the tree, " Titty's dead, and Tatty weeps, the stool hops, and the broom sweeps, the door jars, and the window creaks, the old form runs round the house, and so I shed my leaves."

" Then," said the little bird, " I'll moult all my feathers," so he moulted all his pretty feathers. Now there was a little girl walking below, carrying a jug of milk for her brothers and sisters' supper, and when she saw the poor little bird moult all its feathers, she said : " Little bird, why do you moult all your feathers ? " " Oh ! " said the little bird, " Titty's dead, and Tatty weeps, the stool hops, and the broom sweeps, the door jars, and the window creaks, the old form runs round the house, the walnut-tree sheds its leaves, and so I moult all my feathers."

" So I moult all my feathers."

"Then," said the little girl, "I'll spill the milk," so she dropt the pitcher and spilt the milk.   Now there was an old man just by on the top of a ladder thatching a rick,

" So I spill the milk."

and when he saw the little girl spill the milk, he said : " Little girl, what do you mean by spilling the milk, your little brothers and sisters must go without their supper." Then said the little girl : "Titty's dead, and Tatty weeps, the stool hops, and the broom sweeps, the door jars, and the window creaks, the old form runs round the house, the walnut-tree sheds all its leaves, the little bird moults all its feathers, and so I spill the milk."

So he tumbled off the ladder.

"Oh!" said the old man, "then I'll tumble off the ladder and break my neck," so he tumbled off the ladder and broke his neck ; and when the old man broke his neck, the great walnut-tree fell down with a crash, and upset the old form and house, and the house falling knocked the window out, and the window knocked the door down, and the door upset the broom, and the broom upset the stool, and poor little Tatty Mouse was buried beneath the ruins.

Jack and his Golden Snuff-Box

ONCE upon a time, and a very good time it was, though it was neither in my time nor in your time nor in any one else's time, there was an old man and an old woman, and they had one son, and they lived in a great forest. And their son never saw any other people in his life, but he knew that there were some more in the world besides his own father and mother, because he had lots of books, and he used to read every day about them. And when he read about charming princesses, he would go wild to see some of them; till one day, when his father was out cutting wood, he told his mother that he wished to go away to look for his living in some other country, and to see some other people besides them two. And he said, " I see nothing at all here but great trees around me; and if I stay here, maybe I shall go mad before I see anything." The young man's father was out all the time when this talk was going on between him and his poor old mother.

The old woman began by saying to her son before leaving, " Well, well, my poor boy, if you want to go, it's better for you to go, and God be with you."—(The old woman thought for the best when she said that.)—" But stop a bit before you go.   Which would you like best for me to make you, a little cake and bless you, or a big cake and curse you ? "   " Dear, dear ! " said he, "make me a big cake.   Maybe I shall be hungry on the road." The old woman made the big cake, and she went on top of the house, and she cursed him as far as she could see him.

He presently met with his father, and the old man said to him : " Where are you going, my poor boy ? " when the son told the father the same tale as he told his mother.   " Well," said his father, " I'm sorry to see you going away, but if you've made your mind to go, it's better for you to go."

The poor lad had not gone far, when his father called him back ; then the old man drew out of his pocket a golden snuff-box, and said to him : " Here, take this little box, and put it in your pocket, and be sure not to open it till you are near your death."   And away went poor Jack upon his road, and walked till he was tired and hungry, for he had eaten all his cake upon the road ; and by this time night was upon him, so he could hardly see his way before him.   He could see some light a long way before him, and he made up to it, and found the back door and knocked at it, till one of the maid-servants came and asked him what he wanted.   He said that night was on him, and he wanted to get some place to sleep.   The maid-servant called him in to the fire, and gave him plenty to eat, good meat and bread and beer; and as he was eating his food by the fire, there came the young lady to look at him, and she loved him well and he loved her. And the young lady ran to tell her father, and said there was a pretty young man in the back kitchen; and immediately the gentleman came to him, and questioned him, and asked what work he could do. Jack said, the silly fellow, that he could do anything. (He meant that he could do any foolish bit of work, that would be wanted about the house.)

"Well," says the gentleman to him, "if you can do anything, at eight o'clock in the morning I must have a great lake and some of the largest man-of-war vessels sailing before my mansion, and one of the largest vessels must fire a royal salute, and the last round must break the leg of the bed where my young daughter is sleeping. And if you don't do that, you will have to forfeit your life."

" All right," said Jack; and away he went to his bed, and said his prayers quietly, and slept till it was near eight o'clock, and he had hardly any time to think what he was to do, till all of a sudden he remembered about the little golden box that his father gave him. And he said to himself: " Well, well, I never was so near my death as I am now;" and then he felt in his pocket, and drew the little box out. And when he opened it, out there hopped three little red men, and asked Jack: "What is your will with us?" "Well," said Jack, "I want a great lake and some of the largest man-of-war vessels in the world before this mansion, and one of the largest vessels to fire a royal salute, and the last round to break one of the legs of the bed where this young lady is sleeping." "All right," said the little men ; "go to sleep."

Jack had hardly time to bring the words out of his mouth, to tell the little men what to do, but what it struck eight o'clock, when Bang, bang went one of the largest

man-of-war vessels ; and it made Jack jump out of bed to look through the window ; and I can assure you it was a wonderful sight for him to see, after being so long with his father and mother living in a wood.

By this time Jack dressed himself, and said his prayers, and came down laughing ; for he was proud, he was, because the thing was done so well. The gentleman

comes to him, and says to him : " Well, my young man, I
must say that you are very clever indeed.   Come and
have some breakfast."   And the gentleman tells him,
" Now there are two more things you have to do, and
then you shall have my daughter in marriage."   Jack took
his breakfast, and had a good look at the young lady,
and also she at him.

The other thing that the gentleman told him to do
was to fell all the great trees for miles around by eight
o'clock in the morning ; and, to make my long story
short, it was done, and it pleased the gentleman well.
The gentleman said to him : " The other thing you have
to do "—(and it was the last thing)—" you must get me
a great castle standing on twelve golden pillars ; and
there must come regiments of soldiers and go through
their drill.   At eight o'clock the commanding officer
must say, ' Shoulder up.' "   " All right," said Jack ; when
the third and last morning came the third great feat
was finished, and he had the young daughter in marriage.
But, oh dear ! there was worse to come yet.

The gentleman now made a large hunting party, and
invites all the gentlemen around the country to it, and to
see the castle as well.   And by this time Jack had a
beautiful horse and a scarlet dress to go with them.   On
that morning his valet, when putting Jack's clothes by,
after changing them to go a hunting, put his hand in one
of Jack's waistcoat-pockets, and pulled out the little golden
snuffbox poor Jack had left behind by mistake.   And
that man opened the little box, and there hopped out
the three little red men, and asked him what he wanted
with them.   " Well," said the valet to them, " I want this

castle to be moved from this place far and far across the sea." "All right," said the little red men to him ; "do you wish to go with it ? " "Yes," said he. "Well, get up," said they to him ; and away they went far and far over the great sea.

Now the grand hunting party came back, and the castle upon the twelve golden pillars had disappeared, to the great disappointment of those gentlemen who did not see it before. Poor silly Jack was threatened to have his beautiful young wife taken from him, for deceiving them as he did. But the gentleman at last made an agreement with him, and he was to have a twelvemonths and a day to look for it ; and off he went with a good horse and money in his pocket.

So off poor Jack starts in search of his missing castle, over hills, dales, valleys, and mountains, through woolly woods and sheepwalks, further than I can tell you or ever intend to tell you. Until at last he comes up to the place where lives the King of all the little mice in the world. There was one of the little mice on sentry at the front gate going up to the palace, and he did try to stop Jack from going in. Jack asked the little mouse: "Where does the King live ? I should like to see him." This one sent another with him to show him the place ; and when the King saw him, he called him in. And the King questioned him, and asked him where he was going that way. Well, Jack told him all the truth, that he had lost the great castle, and was going to look for it, and he had a whole twelvemonths and a day to find it out. And Jack asked him whether he knew anything about it ; and the King said : "No, but I am the King of all the little mice in the world, and I will call them all up in the morning, and maybe they have seen something of it."

Then Jack got a good meal and bed, and in the morning he and the King went on to the fields ; and the King called all the mice together, and asked them whether they had seen the great beautiful castle standing on golden pillars. And all the little mice said, No, there was none of them had seen it. The old King said to him that he had two other brothers : " One is the King of all the frogs ; and my other brother, who is the oldest, he is the King of all the birds in the world. And if you go there, may be they know something about the missing castle." The King said to him : " Leave your horse here with me till you come back, and take one of my best horses under you, and give this cake to my brother ; he will know then who you got it from. Mind and tell him I am well, and should like dearly to see him." And then the King and Jack shook hands together.

And when Jack was going through the gates, the little mouse asked him, should he go with him ; and Jack said to him : " No, I shall get myself into trouble with the King." And the little thing told him : " It will be better for you to let me go with you ; maybe I shall do some good to you some time without you knowing it." " Jump up, then." And the little mouse ran up the horse's leg, and made it dance ; and Jack put the mouse in his pocket.

Now Jack, after wishing good morning to the King and pocketing the little mouse which was on sentry, trudged on his way ; and such a long way he had to go

and this was his first day.   At last he found the place ;
and there was one of the frogs on sentry, and gun upon
his shoulder, and he did try to hinder Jack from going in ;
but when Jack said to him that he wanted to see the
King, he allowed him to pass ; and Jack made up to the
door.   The King came out, and asked him his business ;
and Jack told him all from beginning to end.   " Well,
well, come in."   He got good entertainment that night ;
and in the morning the King made such a funny sound,
and collected all the frogs in the world.   And he asked
them, did they know or see anything of a castle that
stood upon twelve golden pillars ; and they all made a
curious sound, *Kro-kro, kro-kro*, and said, No.

Jack had to take another horse, and a cake to this
King's brother, who is the King of all the fowls of the air ;
and as Jack was going through the gates, the little frog
that was on sentry asked him should he go with him.
Jack refused him for a bit ; but at last he told him to
jump up, and Jack put him in his other waistcoat pocket.
And away he went again on his great long journey ; it
was three times as long this time as it was the first day ;
however, he found the place, and there was a fine bird on
sentry.   And Jack passed him, and he never said a word
to him ; and he talked with the King, and told him
everything, all about the castle.   " Well," said the King
to him, " you shall know in the morning from my birds
whether they know anything or not."   Jack put up his
horse in the stable, and then went to bed, after having
something to eat.   And when he got up in the morning
the King and he went on to the fields, and there the
King made some funny noise, and there came all the fowls

THE CASTLE ON TWELVE GOLDEN PILLARS

that were in all the world. And the King asked them ;
" Did they see the fine castle ? " and all the birds answered,
No. " Well," said the King, " Where is the great bird ? "
They had to wait then for a long time for the eagle to make
his appearance, when at last he came all in a perspiration,
after two little birds had been sent high up in the sky to
whistle on him to make all the haste he possibly could.
The King asked the great bird, Did he see the great
castle ? and the bird said : " Yes, I came from there where
it now is." " Well," said the King to him, " this young
gentleman has lost it, and you must go with him back to
it ; but stop till you get a bit of something to eat first."

They killed a calf, and sent the best part of it to feed
the eagle on his journey over the seas, and he had to carry
Jack on his back. Now when they came in sight of the
castle, they did not know what to do to get the little
golden box. Well, the little mouse said to them : " Leave
me down, and I will get the little box for you." So the
mouse stole into the castle, and got hold of the box ;
and when he was coming down the stairs, it fell down,
and he was very near being caught. He came running
out with it, laughing his best. " Have you got it ? "
Jack said to him ; he said : " Yes ; " and off they went
back again, and left the castle behind.

As they were all of them (Jack, mouse, frog, and eagle)
passing over the great sea, they fell to quarrelling about
which it was that got the little box, till down it slipped
into the water. (It was by their looking at it and
handing it from one hand to the other that they dropped
the little box to the bottom of the sea.) " Well, well,"
said the frog, " I knew that I would have to do something,

so you had better let me go down in the water." And
they let him go, and he was down for three days and
three nights ; and up he comes, and shows his nose and
little mouth out of the water ; and all of them asked him,
Did he get it ? and he told them, No.   "Well, what are
you doing there, then ? "   " Nothing at all," he said, " only
I want my full breath ; " and the poor little frog went
down the second time, and he was down for a day and a
night, and up he brings it.

And away they did go, after being there four days
and nights ; and after a long tug over seas and mountains,
arrived at the palace of the old King, who is the master of
all the birds in the world.   And the King was very proud to
see them, and had a hearty welcome and a long conversa-
tion.   Jack opened the little box, and told the little men to
go back and to bring the castle here to them ; " and all of
you make as much haste back again as you possibly can."

The three little men went off ; and when they came
near the castle they were afraid to go to it till the
gentleman and lady and all the servants were gone out
to some dance.   And there was no one left behind there,
only the cook and another maid with her ; and the little
red men asked them which would they rather—go, or stop
behind ? and they both said : " I will go with you ; "
and the little men told them to run upstairs quick.
They were no sooner up and in one of the drawing-
rooms than there came just in sight the gentleman and
lady and all the servants ; but it was too late.   Off the
castle went at full speed, with the women laughing at
them through the window, while they made motions for
them to stop, but all to no purpose.

They were nine days on their journey, in which they did try to keep the Sunday holy, when one of the little men turned to be the priest, the other the clerk, and third preside at the organ, and the women were the singers, for they had a grand chapel in the castle already. Strange to say, there was a discord made in the music, and one of the little men ran up one of the organ-pipes to see where the bad sound came from, when he found out it only happened to be that the two women were laughing at the little red man stretching his little legs full length on the bass pipes, also his two arms the same time, with his little red nightcap, which he never forgot to wear, a sight they never witnessed before, and which could not help making them laugh long and loud and heartily. And poor things! through their not going on with what they begun, they very near came to danger, as the castle was once all but sinking in the middle of the sea.

At length, after a merry journey, they came again to Jack and the King. The King was quite struck with the sight of the castle; and going up the golden stairs, went to see the inside.

The King was very much pleased with the castle, but poor Jack's time of a twelvemonths and a day was drawing to a close; and he, wishing to go home to his young wife, gave orders to the three little men to get ready by the next morning at eight o'clock to be off to the next brother, and to stop there for one night; also to proceed from there to the last or the youngest brother, the master of all the mice in the world, in such place where the castle should be left under his care until it's sent for.   Jack took a farewell of the King, thanking him very much for his hospitality.

Away went Jack and his castle again, and stopped one night in that place ; and away they went again to the third King, and there left the castle under his care.   As Jack had to leave the castle behind, he had to take to his own horse, which he left there when he first started.

So our poor Jack leaves his castle behind and faces towards home ; and after having so much merriment with the three brothers every night, Jack became sleepy on horseback, and would have lost the road if it was not for the little men a-guiding him.   At last he arrived weary and tired, and they did not seem to receive him with any kindness whatever, because he had not found the stolen castle ; and to make it worse, he was disappointed in not seeing his young and beautiful wife come out and meet him, hindered as she was by her parents.   But that did not stop long.   Jack put full power on and set off with the little men to bring on the castle, and they soon got there.

Jack shook hands with the King, and returned many thanks for his kingly kindness in minding the castle for him ; and then Jack instructed the little men to spur up and put speed on.   And off they went, and were not long before they reached their journey's end, when out comes the young wife to meet him with a fine jolly, bonny young SON, and they all lived happy ever afterwards.

The Story of the Three Bears

ONCE upon a time there were Three Bears, who lived together in a house of their own, in a wood. One of them was a Little, Small Wee Bear; and one was a Middle-sized Bear, and the other was a Great, Huge Bear. They had each a pot for their porridge, a little pot for the Little, Small, Wee Bear; and a middle-sized pot for the Middle Bear, and a great pot for the Great, Huge Bear. And they had each a chair to sit in; a little chair for the Little, Small, Wee Bear; and a middle-sized chair for the Middle Bear; and a great chair for the Great, Huge Bear. And they had each a bed to sleep in ; a little bed for the Little, Small, Wee Bear ; and a middle-sized bed for the Middle Bear; and a great bed for the Great, Huge Bear.

One day, after they had made the porridge for their breakfast, and poured it into their porridge-pots, they walked out into the wood while the porridge was cooling, that they might not burn their mouths, by beginning too soon to eat it. And while they were walking, a little old Woman came to the house. She could not have been a good, honest old Woman ; for first she looked in at the window, and then she peeped in at the keyhole ; and seeing nobody in the house, she lifted the latch. The door was not fastened, because the Bears were good Bears, who did nobody any harm, and never suspected that anybody would harm them. So the little old Woman opened the door, and went in ; and well pleased she was when she saw the porridge on the table. If she had been a good little old Woman, she would have waited till the Bears came home, and then, perhaps, they would have asked her to breakfast ; for they were good Bears—a little rough or so, as the manner of Bears is, but for all that very good-natured and hospitable. But she was an impudent, bad old Woman, and set about helping herself.

So first she tasted the porridge of the Great, Huge Bear, and that was too hot for her ; and she said a bad word about that. And then she tasted the porridge of the Middle Bear, and that was too cold for her ; and she said a bad word about that too. And then she went to the porridge of the Little, Small, Wee Bear, and tasted that ; and that was neither too hot, nor too cold, but just right; and she liked it so well, that she ate it all up: but the naughty old Woman said a bad word about the little porridge-pot, because it did not hold enough for her.

Then the little old Woman sate down in the chair of the Great, Huge Bear, and that was too hard for her. And then she sate down in the chair of the Middle Bear, and that was too soft for her. And then she sat down in the chair of the Little, Small, Wee Bear, and that was neither too hard, nor too soft, but just right. So she seated herself in it, and there she sate till the bottom of the chair came out, and down she came, plump upon the ground. And the naughty old Woman said a wicked word about that too.

Then the little old Woman went upstairs into the bed-chamber in which the three Bears slept. And 'first she lay down upon the bed of the Great, Huge Bear; but that was too high at the head for her. And next she lay down upon the bed of the Middle Bear; and that was too high at the foot for her. And then she lay down upon the bed of the Little, Small, Wee Bear; and that was neither too high at the head, nor at the foot, but just right. So she covered herself up comfortably, and lay there till she fell fast asleep.

By this time the Three Bears thought their porridge would be cool enough; so they came home to breakfast. Now the little old Woman had left the spoon of the Great, Huge Bear, standing in his porridge.

"Somebody has been at my porridge!"

said the Great, Huge Bear, in his great, rough, gruff voice. And when the Middle Bear looked at his, he saw that the spoon was standing in it too.   They were wooden spoons ; if they had been silver ones, the naughty old Woman would have put them in her pocket.

"Somebody has been at my porridge!"

said the Middle Bear in his middle voice.

Then the Little, Small, Wee Bear looked at his, and there was the spoon in the porridge-pot, but the porridge was all gone.

"Somebody has been at my porridge, and has eaten it all up!"

said the Little, Small, Wee Bear, in his little, small, wee voice.

Upon this the Three Bears, seeing that some one had entered their house, and eaten up the Little, Small, Wee Bear's breakfast, began to look about them.   Now the little old Woman had not put the hard cushion straight when she rose from the chair of the Great, Huge Bear.

"Somebody has been sitting in my chair!"

said the Great, Huge Bear, in his great, rough, gruff voice.

And the little old Woman had squatted down the soft cushion of the Middle Bear.

"Somebody has been sitting in my chair!"

said the Middle Bear, in his middle voice.

And you know what the little old Woman had done to the third chair.

"Somebody has been sitting in my chair and has sate the bottom out of it!"

said the Little, Small, Wee Bear, in his little, small, wee voice.

Then the Three Bears thought it necessary that they should make farther search; so they went upstairs into their bedchamber. Now the little old Woman had pulled the pillow of the Great, Huge Bear, out of its place.

"Somebody has been lying in my bed!"

said the Great, Huge Bear, in his great, rough, gruff voice.

And the little old Woman had pulled the bolster of the Middle Bear out of its place.

"Somebody has been lying in my bed!"

said the Middle Bear, in his middle voice.

And when the Little, Small, Wee Bear came to look at his bed, there was the bolster in its place; and the pillow in its place upon the bolster; and upon the pillow was the little old Woman's ugly, dirty head,—which was not in its place, for she had no business there.

"Somebody has been lying in my bed,—and here she is!"

said the Little, Small, Wee Bear, in his little, small, wee voice.

The little old Woman had heard in her sleep the great, rough, gruff voice of the Great, Huge Bear; but she was so fast asleep that it was no more to her than the roaring of wind, or the rumbling of thunder. And she had heard the middle voice, of the Middle Bear, but it was only as if she had heard some one speaking in a dream. But when she heard the little, small, wee voice of the Little, Small, Wee Bear, it was so sharp, and so shrill, that it awakened her at once. Up she started and when she saw the Three Bears on one side of the bed, she tumbled herself out at the other, and ran to the window. Now the window was open, because the Bears, like good, tidy Bears, as they were, always opened their bedchamber window when they got up in the morning. Out the little old Woman jumped; and whether she broke her neck in the fall; or ran into the wood and was lost there; or found her way out of the wood, and was taken up by the constable and sent to the House of Correction for a vagrant as she was, I cannot tell. But the Three Bears never saw anything more of her.

Jack the Giant-Killer

WHEN good King Arthur reigned, there lived near the Land's End of England, in the county of Cornwall, a farmer who had one only son called Jack. He was brisk and of a ready lively wit, so that nobody or nothing could worst him.

In those days the Mount of Cornwall was kept by a huge giant named Cormoran. He was eighteen feet in height, and about three yards round the waist, of a fierce and grim countenance, the terror of all the neighbouring towns and villages. He lived in a cave in the midst of the Mount, and whenever he wanted food he would wade over to the main-land, where he would furnish himself with whatever came in his way. Everybody at his approach ran out of their houses, while he seized on their cattle, making nothing of carrying half-a-dozen oxen on his back at a time; and as for their sheep and hogs, he would tie them round his waist like a bunch of tallow-dips. He had done this for many years, so that all Cornwall was in despair.

One day Jack happened to be at the town-hall when the magistrates were sitting in council about the Giant. He asked: "What reward will be given to the man who kills Cormoran?" "The giant's treasure," they said, "will be the reward." Quoth Jack: "Then let me undertake it."

So he got a horn, shovel, and pickaxe, and went over to the Mount in the beginning of a dark winter's evening, when he fell to work, and before morning had dug a pit twenty-two feet deep, and nearly as broad, covering it over with long sticks and straw. Then he strewed a little mould over it, so that it appeared like plain ground. Jack then placed himself on the opposite side of the pit, farthest from the giant's lodging, and, just at the break of day, he put the horn to his mouth, and blew, Tantivy, Tantivy. This noise roused the giant, who rushed from his cave, crying: "You incorrigible villain, are you come here to disturb my rest? You shall pay dearly for this. Satisfaction I will have, and this it shall be, I will take you whole and broil you for breakfast." He had no sooner uttered this, than he tumbled into the pit, and made the very foundations of the Mount to shake. "Oh, Giant," quoth Jack, "where are you now? Oh, faith, you are gotten now into Lob's Pound, where I will surely plague you for your threatening words: what do you think now of broiling me for your breakfast? Will no other diet serve you but poor Jack?" Then having tantalised the giant for a while, he gave him a most weighty knock with his pickaxe on the very crown of his head, and killed him on the spot.

Jack then filled up the pit with earth, and went to search the cave, which he found contained much treasure. When the magistrates heard of this they made a declaration he should henceforth be termed

JACK THE GIANT-KILLER,

and presented him with a sword and a belt, on which were written these words embroidered in letters of gold :

> "Here's the right valiant Cornish man,
> Who slew the giant Cormoran."

The news of Jack's victory soon spread over all the West of England, so that another giant, named Blunderbore, hearing of it, vowed to be revenged on Jack, if ever he should light on him. This giant was the lord of an enchanted castle situated in the midst of a lonesome wood. Now Jack, about four months afterwards, walking near this wood in his journey to Wales, being weary, seated himself near a pleasant fountain and fell fast asleep. While he was sleeping, the giant, coming there for water, discovered him, and knew him to be the far-famed Jack the Giant-killer by the lines written on the belt. Without ado, he took Jack on his shoulders and carried him towards his castle. Now, as they passed through a thicket, the rustling of the boughs awakened Jack, who was strangely surprised to find himself in the clutches of the giant. His terror was only begun, for, on entering the castle, he saw the ground strewed with human bones, and the giant told him his own would ere long be among them. After this the giant locked poor Jack in an immense chamber, leaving him there while he went to fetch another giant, his brother, living in the same wood, who might share in the meal on Jack.

After waiting some time Jack, on going to the window beheld afar off the two giants coming towards the castle. "Now," quoth Jack to himself, "my death or my deliverance is at hand." Now, there were strong cords in a corner of the room in which Jack was, and two of these he took, and made a strong noose at the end; and while the giants were unlocking the iron gate of the castle he threw the ropes over each of their heads. Then he drew the other ends across a beam, and pulled with all his might, so that he throttled them. Then, when he saw they were black in the face, he slid down the rope, and drawing his sword, slew them both. Then, taking the giant's keys, and unlocking the rooms, he found three fair ladies tied by the hair of their heads, almost starved to death. "Sweet ladies," quoth Jack, "I have destroyed this monster and his brutish brother, and obtained your liberties." This said he presented them with the keys, and so proceeded on his journey to Wales.

Jack made the best of his way by travelling as fast as he could, but lost his road, and was benighted, and could find no habitation until, coming into a narrow valley, he found a large house, and in order to get shelter took courage to knock at the gate. But what was his surprise when there came forth a monstrous giant with two heads; yet he did not appear so fiery as the others were, for he was a Welsh giant, and what he did was by private and secret malice under the false show of friendship. Jack, having told his condition to the giant, was shown into a bedroom, where, in the dead of night, he heard his host in another apartment muttering these words :

> "Though here you lodge with me this night,
> You shall not see the morning light :
> My club shall dash your brains outright !'

"Say'st thou so," quoth Jack; "that is like one of your Welsh tricks, yet I hope to be cunning enough for you." Then, getting out of bed, he laid a billet in the bed in his stead, and hid himself in a corner of the room. At the dead time of the night in came the Welsh giant, who struck several heavy blows on the bed with his club, thinking he had broken every bone in Jack's skin. The next morning Jack, laughing in his sleeve, gave him hearty thanks for his night's lodging. "How have you rested ?" quoth the giant ; "did you not feel anything in the night ?" "No," quoth Jack, "nothing but a rat, which gave me two or three slaps with her tail." With that, greatly wondering, the giant led Jack to breakfast, bringing him a bowl containing four gallons of hasty pudding. Being loth to let the giant think it too much for him, Jack put a large leather bag under his loose coat, in such a way that he could convey the pudding into it without its being perceived. Then, telling the giant he would show him a trick, taking a knife, Jack ripped open the bag, and out came all the hasty pudding. Whereupon, saying, "Odds splutters hur nails, hur can do that trick hursclf," the monster took the knife, and ripping open his belly, fell down dead.

Now, it happened in these days that King Arthur's only son asked his father to give him a large sum of money, in order that he might go and seek his fortune in the principality of Wales, where lived a beautiful lady

possessed with seven evil spirits.   The king did his best
to persuade his son from it, but in vain ; so at last gave
way and the prince set out with two horses, one loaded
with money, the other for himself to ride upon.   Now,
after several days' travel, he came to a market-town in
Wales, where he beheld a vast crowd of people gathered
together.   The prince asked the reason of it, and was
told that they had arrested a corpse for several large
sums of money which the deceased owed when he died.
The prince replied that it was a pity creditors should be
so cruel, and said : " Go bury the dead, and let his
creditors come to my lodging, and there their debts shall
be paid."   They came, in such great numbers that before
night he had only twopence left for himself.

Now Jack the Giant-Killer, coming that way, was so
taken with the generosity of the prince, that he desired to
be his servant.   This being agreed upon, the next
morning they set forward on their journey together,
when, as they were riding out of the town, an old woman
called after the prince, saying, " He has owed me twopence these seven years ; pray pay me as well as the
rest."   Putting his hand to his pocket, the prince gave
the woman all he had left, so that after their day's food,
which cost what small store Jack had by him, they were
without a penny between them.

When the sun got low, the king's son said : " Jack, since
we have no money, where can we lodge this night ? "

But Jack replied : " Master, we'll do well enough, for I
have an uncle lives within two miles of this place ; he is a
huge and monstrous giant with three heads ; he'll fight five
hundred men in armour, and make them to fly before him."

"Alas!" quoth the prince, "what shall we do there? He'll certainly chop us up at a mouthful. Nay, we are scarce enough to fill one of his hollow teeth!"

"It is no matter for that," quoth Jack; "I myself will go before and prepare the way for you; therefore stop here and wait till I return." Jack then rode away at full speed, and coming to the gate of the castle, he knocked so loud that he made the neighbouring hills resound. The giant roared out at this like thunder: "Who's there?"

Jack answered: "None but your poor cousin Jack."

Quoth he: "What news with my poor cousin Jack?"

He replied: "Dear uncle, heavy news, God wot!"

"Prithee," quoth the giant, "what heavy news can come to me? I am a giant with three heads, and besides thou knowest I can fight five hundred men in armour, and make them fly like chaff before the wind."

"Oh, but," quoth Jack, "here's the king's son a-coming with a thousand men in armour to kill you and destroy all that you have!"

"Oh, cousin Jack," said the giant, "this is heavy news indeed! I will immediately run and hide myself, and thou shalt lock, bolt, and bar me in, and keep the keys until the prince is gone." Having secured the giant, Jack fetched his master, when they made themselves heartily merry whilst the poor giant lay trembling in a vault under the ground.

Early in the morning Jack furnished his master with a fresh supply of gold and silver, and then sent him three miles forward on his journey, at which time the prince was pretty well out of the smell of the giant. Jack then returned, and let the giant out of the vault, who asked what he should give him for keeping the castle from destruction. "Why," quoth Jack, "I want nothing but the old coat and cap, together with the old rusty sword and slippers which are at your bed's head." Quoth the giant: "You know not what you ask; they are the most precious things I have. The coat will keep you invisible, the cap will tell you all you want to know, the sword cuts asunder whatever you strike, and the shoes are of extraordinary swiftness. But you have been very serviceable to me, therefore take them with all my heart." Jack thanked his uncle, and then went off with them. He soon overtook his master and they quickly arrived at the house of the lady the prince sought, who, finding the prince to be a suitor, prepared a splendid banquet for him. After the repast was concluded, she told him she had a task for him. She wiped his mouth with a handkerchief, saying: "You must show me that handkerchief to-morrow morning, or else you will lose your head." With that she put it in her bosom. The prince went to bed in great sorrow, but Jack's cap of knowledge informed him how it was to be obtained. In the middle of the night she called upon her familiar spirit to carry her to Lucifer. But Jack put on his coat of darkness and his shoes of swiftness, and was there as soon as she was. When she entered the place of the demon, she gave the handkerchief to him, and he laid it upon a shelf, whence Jack took it and brought it to his master, who showed it to the lady next day, and so saved his life. On that day, she gave the prince a kiss and told him he must show her the lips to-morrow morning that she kissed last night, or lose his head.

"Ah!" he replied, "if you kiss none but mine, I will."

"That is neither here nor there," said she; "if you do not, death's your portion!"

At midnight she went as before, and was angry with the demon for letting the handkerchief go. "But now," quoth she, "I will be too hard for the king's son, for I will kiss thee, and he is to show me thy lips." Which she did, and Jack, when she was not standing by, cut off Lucifer's head and brought it under his invisible coat to his master, who the next morning pulled it out by the horns before the lady. This broke the enchantment and the evil spirit left her, and she appeared in all her beauty. They were married the next morning, and soon after went to the court of King Arthur, where Jack for his many great exploits, was made one of the Knights of the Round Table.

Jack soon went searching for giants again, but he had not ridden far, when he saw a cave, near the entrance of which he beheld a giant sitting upon a block of timber, with a knotted iron club by his side. His goggle eyes were like flames of fire, his countenance grim and ugly, and his cheeks like a couple of large flitches of bacon, while the bristles of his beard resembled rods of iron wire, and the locks that hung down upon his brawny shoulders were like curled snakes or hissing adders. Jack alighted from his horse, and, putting on the coat of darkness, went up close to the giant, and said softly: "Oh! are you there? It will not be long before I take you fast by the beard." The giant all this while could not see him, on account of his invisible coat, so that Jack, coming up close to the monster, struck a blow with his sword at his head, but, missing his aim, he cut off the nose instead. At this, the giant roared like claps of thunder, and began to lay about him with his iron club like one stark mad. But Jack, running behind, drove his sword up to the hilt in the giant's back, so that he fell down dead. This done, Jack cut off the giant's head, and sent it, with his brother's also, to King Arthur, by a waggoner he hired for that purpose.

Jack now resolved to enter the giant's cave in search of his treasure, and, passing along through a great many windings and turnings, he came at length to a large room paved with freestone, at the upper end of which was a boiling caldron, and on the right hand a large table, at which the giant used to dine. Then he came to a window, barred with iron, through which he looked and beheld a vast number of miserable captives, who, seeing him, cried out: "Alas! young man, art thou come to be one amongst us in this miserable den?"

"Ay," quoth Jack, "but pray tell me what is the meaning of your captivity?"

"We are kept here," said one, "till such time as the giants have a wish to feast, and then the fattest among us is slaughtered! And many are the times they have dined upon murdered men!"

"Say you so," quoth Jack, and straightway unlocked the gate and let them free, who all rejoiced like condemned men at sight of a pardon. Then searching the giant's coffers, he shared the gold and silver equally amongst them and took them to a neighbouring castle, where they all feasted and made merry over their deliverance.

But in the midst of all this mirth a messenger brought

news that one Thunderdell, a giant with two heads, having heard of the death of his kinsmen, had come from the northern dales to be revenged on Jack, and was within a mile of the castle, the country people flying before him like chaff. But Jack was not a bit daunted, and said: "Let him come! I have a tool to pick his teeth ; and you, ladies and gentlemen, walk out into the garden, and you shall witness this giant Thunderdell's death and destruction."

The castle was situated in the midst of a small island surrounded by a moat thirty feet deep and twenty feet wide, over which lay a drawbridge. So Jack employed men to cut through this bridge on both sides, nearly to the middle ; and then, dressing himself in his invisible coat, he marched against the giant with his sword of sharpness. Although the giant could not see Jack, he smelt his approach, and cried out in these words :

> "Fee, fi, fo, fum !
> I smell the blood of an Englishman !
> Be he alive or be he dead,
> I'll grind his bones to make me bread !"

"Say'st thou so," said Jack ; "then thou art a monstrous miller indeed."

The giant cried out again : "Art thou that villain who killed my kinsmen ? Then I will tear thee with my teeth, suck thy blood, and grind thy bones to powder."

"You'll have to catch me first," quoth Jack, and throwing off his invisible coat, so that the giant might see him, and putting on his shoes of swiftness, he ran from the giant, who followed like a walking castle, so that the very foundations of the earth seemed to shake at every step.

Jack led him a long dance, in order that the gentlemen
and ladies might see ; and at last to end the matter, ran
lightly over the drawbridge, the giant, in full speed,
pursuing him with his club. Then, coming to the middle
of the bridge, the giant's great weight broke it down, and
he tumbled headlong into the water, where he rolled and
wallowed like a whale. Jack, standing by the moat,
laughed at him all the while ; but though the giant
foamed to hear him scoff, and plunged from place to
place in the moat, yet he could not get out to be revenged.
Jack at length got a cart-rope and cast it over the two
heads of the giant, and drew him ashore by a team of
horses, and then cut off both his heads with his sword of
sharpness, and sent them to King Arthur.

After some time spent in mirth and pastime, Jack,
taking leave of the knights and ladies, set out for new
adventures. Through many woods he passed, and came
at length to the foot of a high mountain. Here, late at
night, he found a lonesome house, and knocked at the
door, which was opened by an aged man with a head as
white as snow. " Father," said Jack, " can you lodge a
benighted traveller that has lost his way ? " " Yes," said
the old man ; " you are right welcome to my poor
cottage." Whereupon Jack entered, and down they
sat together, and the old man began to speak as
follows : " Son, I see by your belt you are the
great conqueror of giants, and behold, my son, on the
top of this mountain is an enchanted castle, this is
kept by a giant named Galligantua, and he by the
help of an old conjurer, betrays many knights and
ladies into his castle, where by magic art they are

JACK WITH HIS INVISIBLE COAT.

transformed into sundry shapes and forms. But above all, I grieve for a duke's daughter, whom they fetched from her father's garden, carrying her through the air in a burning chariot drawn by fiery dragons, when they secured her within the castle, and transformed her into a white hind. And though many knights have tried to break the enchantment, and work her deliverance, yet no one could accomplish it, on account of two dreadful griffins which are placed at the castle gate and which destroy every one who comes near. But you, my son, may pass by them undiscovered, where on the gates of the castle you will find engraven in large letters how the spell may be broken." Jack gave the old man his hand, and promised that in the morning he would venture his life to free the lady.

In the morning Jack arose and put on his invisible coat and magic cap and shoes, and prepared himself for the fray. Now, when he had reached the top of the mountain he soon discovered the two fiery griffins, but passed them without fear, because of his invisible coat. When he had got beyond them, he found upon the gates of the castle a golden trumpet hung by a silver chain, under which these lines were engraved :

> " Whoever shall this trumpet blow,
> Shall soon the giant overthrow,
> And break the black enchantment straight ;
> So all shall be in happy state."

Jack had no sooner read this but he blew the trumpet, at which the castle trembled to its vast foundations, and the giant and conjurer were in horrid confusion, biting their thumbs and tearing their hair, knowing their wicked reign was at an end. Then the giant stooping to take up his club, Jack at one blow cut off his head ; whereupon the conjurer, mounting up into the air, was carried away in a whirlwind. Then the enchantment was broken, and all the lords and ladies who had so long been transformed into birds and beasts returned to their proper shapes, and the castle vanished away in a cloud of smoke. This being done, the head of Galligantua was likewise, in the usual manner, conveyed to the Court of King Arthur, where, the very next day, Jack followed, with the knights and ladies who had been delivered. Whereupon, as a reward for his good services, the king prevailed upon the duke to bestow his daughter in marriage on honest Jack. So married they were, and the whole kingdom was filled with joy at the wedding. Furthermore, the king bestowed on Jack a noble castle, with a very beautiful estate thereto belonging, where he and his lady lived in great joy and happiness all the rest of their days.

Henny-Penny

ONE day Henny-penny was picking up corn in the cornyard when—whack!—something hit her upon the head. "Goodness gracious me!" said Henny-penny; "the sky's a-going to fall; I must go and tell the king."

So she went along and she went along and she went along till she met Cocky-locky. "Where are you going, Henny-penny?" says Cocky-locky. "Oh! I'm going to tell the king the sky's a-falling," says Henny-penny. "May I come with you?" says Cocky-locky. "Certainly," says Henny-penny. So Henny-penny and Cocky-locky went to tell the king the sky was falling.

They went along, and they went along, and they went along, till they met Ducky-daddles. "Where are you going to, Henny-penny and Cocky-locky?" says Ducky-daddles. "Oh! we're going to tell the king the sky's a-falling," said Henny-penny and Cocky-locky. "May I come with you?" says Ducky-daddles. "Certainly," said Henny-penny and Cocky-locky. So Henny-penny, Cocky-locky and Ducky-daddles went to tell the king the sky was a-falling.

So they went along, and they went along, and they went along, till they met Goosey-poosey, "Where are you going to, Henny-penny, Cocky-locky and Ducky-daddles?" said Goosey-poosey. "Oh!" we're going to tell the king the sky's a-falling," said Henny-penny and Cocky-locky and Ducky-daddles. "May I come with you," said Goosey-poosey. "Certainly," said Henny-penny, Cocky-locky and Ducky-daddles. So Henny-penny, Cocky-locky, Ducky-daddles and Goosy-poosey went to tell the king the sky was a-falling.

So they went along, and they went along, and they went along, till they met Turkey-lurkey. "Where are you going, Henny-penny, Cocky-locky, Ducky-daddles, and Goosey-poosey?" says Turkey-lurkey. "Oh! we're going to tell the king the sky's a-falling," said Henny-penny, Cocky-locky, Ducky-daddles and Goosey-poosey. "May I come with you? Henny-penny, Cocky-locky, Ducky-daddles and Goosey-poosey?" said Turkey-lurkey. "Why, certainly, Turkey-lurkey," said Henny-penny, Cocky-locky, Ducky-daddles, and Goosey-poosey. So Henny-penny, Cocky-locky, Ducky-daddles, Goosey-poosey and Turkey-lurkey all went to tell the king the sky was a-falling.

So they went along, and they went along, and they
went along, till they met Foxy-woxy, and Foxy-woxy
said to Henny-penny, Cocky-locky, Ducky-daddles,
Goosey-poosey and Turkey-lurkey: "Where are you going, Henny-penny, Cocky-locky, Ducky-daddles, Goosey-
poosey, and Turkey-lurkey?" And Henny-penny,
Cocky-locky, Ducky-daddles, Goosey-poosey, and Turkey-
lurkey said to Foxy-woxy: "We're going to tell the king
the sky's a-falling." "Oh! but this is not the way to the
king, Henny-penny, Cocky-locky, Ducky-daddles, Goosey-
poosey and Turkey-lurkey," says Foxy-woxy; "I know
the proper way; shall I show it you?" "Why certainly,
Foxy-woxy," said Henny-penny, Cocky-locky, Ducky-
daddles, Goosey-poosey, and Turkey-lurkey. So Henny-
penny, Cocky-locky, Ducky-daddles, Goosey-poosey,
Turkey-lurkey, and Foxy-woxy all went to tell the king
the sky was a-falling. So they went along, and they
went along, and they went along, till they came to a
narrow and dark hole. Now this was the door of Foxy-
woxy's cave. But Foxy-woxy said to Henny-penny,
Cocky-locky, Ducky-daddles, Goosey-poosey, and Turkey-
lurkey: "This is the short way to the king's palace:
you'll soon get there if you follow me. I will go first and
you come after, Henny-penny, Cocky-locky, Ducky-
daddles, Goosey-poosey, and Turkey-lurkey." "Why of
course, certainly, without doubt, why not?" said Henny-
Penny, Cocky-locky, Ducky-daddles, Goosey-poosey, and
Turkey-lurkey.

So Foxy-woxy went into his cave, and he didn't go
very far but turned round to wait for Henny-Penny,
Cocky-locky, Ducky-daddles, Goosey-poosey and Turkey-

lurkey. So at last at first Turkey-lurkey went through the dark hole into the cave. He hadn't got far when "Hrumph," Foxy-woxy snapped off Turkey-lurkey's head and threw his body over his left shoulder. Then Goosey-poosey went in, and "Hrumph," off went her head and Goosey-poosey was thrown beside Turkey-lurkey. Then Ducky-daddles waddled down, and "Hrumph," snapped Foxy-woxy, and Ducky-daddles' head was off and Ducky-daddles was thrown alongside Turkey-lurkey and Goosey-poosey. Then Cocky-locky strutted down into the cave and he hadn't gone far when "Snap, Hrumph!" went Foxy-woxy and Cocky-locky was thrown alongside of Turkey-lurkey, Goosey-poosey and Ducky-daddles.

But Foxy-woxy had made two bites at Cocky-locky, and when the first snap only hurt Cocky-locky, but didn't kill him, he called out to Henny-penny. So she turned tail and ran back home, so she never told the king the sky was a-falling.

Childe Rowland

CHILDE Rowland and his brothers twain
    Were playing at the ball,
      And there was their sister Burd Ellen
In the midst, among them all.

Childe Rowland kicked it with his foot
    And caught it with his knee ;
At last as he plunged among them all
    O'er the church he made it flee.

Burd Ellen round about the aisle
    To seek the ball is gone,
But long they waited, and longer still,
    And she came not back again.

> They sought her east, they sought her west,
>   They sought her up and down,
> And woe were the hearts of those brethren,
>   For she was not to be found.

So at last her eldest brother went to the Warlock Merlin and told him all the case, and asked him if he knew where Burd Ellen was. "The fair Burd Ellen," said the Warlock Merlin, "must have been carried off by the fairies, because she went round the church 'widershins'—the opposite way to the sun. She is now in the Dark Tower of the King of Elfland; it would take the boldest knight in Christendom to bring her back."

"If it is possible to bring her back," said her brother, "I'll do it, or perish in the attempt."

"Possible it is," said the Warlock Merlin, "but woe to the man or mother's son that attempts it, if he is not well taught beforehand what he is to do."

The eldest brother of Burd Ellen was not to be put off, by any fear of danger, from attempting to get her back, so he begged the Warlock Merlin to tell him what he should do, and what he should not do, in going to seek his sister. And after he had been taught, and had repeated his lesson, he set out for Elfland.

> But long they waited, and longer still,
>   With doubt and muckle pain,
> But woe were the hearts of his brethren,
>   For he came not back again.

Then the second brother got tired and tired of waiting, and he went to the Warlock Merlin and asked him

the same as his brother. So he set out to find Burd
Ellen.

> But long they waited, and longer still,
>   With muckle doubt and pain,
> And woe were his mother's and brother's heart,
>   For he came not back again.

And when they had waited and waited a good long
time, Childe Rowland, the youngest of Burd Ellen's
brothers, wished to go, and went to his mother, the good
queen, to ask her to let him go. But she would not at
first, for he was the last and dearest of her children, and
if he was lost, all would be lost. But he begged, and he
begged, till at last the good queen let him go, and gave
him his father's good brand that never struck in vain.
and as she girt it round his waist, she said the spell that
would give it victory.

So Childe Rowland said good-bye to the good queen, his
mother, and went to the cave of the Warlock Merlin.
" Once more, and but once more," he said to the Warlock,
" tell how man or mother's son may rescue Burd Ellen
and her brothers twain."

" Well, my son," said the Warlock Merlin, " there are
but two things, simple they may seem, but hard they are
to do. One thing to do, and one thing not to do. And
the thing to do is this : after you have entered the land
of Fairy, whoever speaks to you, till you meet the Burd
Ellen, you must out with your father's brand and off with
their head. And what you've not to do is this : bite no
bit, and drink no drop, however hungry or thirsty you

be ; drink a drop, or bite a bit, while in Elfland you be and never will you see Middle Earth again."

So Childe Rowland said the two things over and over again, till he knew them by heart, and he thanked the Warlock Merlin and went on his way. And he went along, and along, and along, and still further along, till he came to the horse-herd of the King of Elfland feeding his horses. These he knew by their fiery eyes, and knew that he was at last in the land of Fairy. " Canst thou tell me," said Childe Rowland to the horse-herd, " where the King of Elfland's Dark Tower is ? " " I cannot tell thee," said the horse-herd, " but go on a little further and thou wilt come to the cow-herd, and he, maybe, can tell thee."

Then, without a word more, Childe Rowland drew the good brand that never struck in vain, and off went the horse-herd's head, and Childe Rowland went on further, till he came to the cow-herd, and asked him the same question. " I can't tell thee," said he, " but go on a little farther, and thou wilt come to the hen-wife, and she is sure to know." Then Childe Rowland out with his good brand, that never struck in vain, and off went the cow-herd's head. And he went on a little further, till he came to an old woman in a grey cloak, and he asked her if she knew where the Dark Tower of the King of Elfland was. " Go on a little further," said the hen-wife, " till you come to a round green hill, surrounded with terrace-rings, from the bottom to the top ; go round it three times, widershins, and each time say :

Open, door ! open, door !
And let me come in.

and the third time the door will open, and you may go in." And Childe Rowland was just going on, when he remembered what he had to do ; so he out with the good brand, that never struck in vain, and off went the hen-wife's head.

Then he went on, and on, and on, till he came to the round green hill with the terrace-rings from top to bottom, and he went round it three times, widershins, saying each time :

Open, door ! open, door !
And let me come in.

And the third time the door did open, and he went in, and it closed with a click, and Childe Rowland was left in the dark.

It was not exactly dark, but a kind of twilight or gloaming. There were neither windows nor candles, and he could not make out where the twilight came from, if not through the walls and roof. These were rough arches made of a transparent rock, incrusted with sheepsilver and rock spar, and other bright stones. But though it was rock, the air was quite warm, as it always is in Elfland. So he went through this passage till at last he came to two wide and high folding-doors which stood ajar. And when he opened them, there he saw a most wonderful and glorious sight. A large and spacious hall, so large that it seemed to be as long, and as broad, as the green hill itself. The roof was supported by fine pillars, so large and lofty, that the pillars of a cathedral were as nothing to them. They were all of gold and silver, with fretted work, and between them and around them wreaths

of flowers, composed of what do you think? Why, of
diamonds and emeralds, and all manner of precious stones.
And the very key-stones of the arches had for ornaments
clusters of diamonds and rubies, and pearls, and other
precious stones. And all these arches met in the middle
of the roof, and just there, hung by a gold chain, an
immense lamp made out of one big pearl hollowed out
and quite transparent. And in the middle of this was a
big, huge carbuncle, which kept spinning round and
round, and this was what gave light by its rays to the
whole hall, which seemed as if the setting sun was shining
on it.

The hall was furnished in a manner equally grand, and
at one end of it was a glorious couch of velvet, silk and
gold, and there sate Burd Ellen, combing her golden hair
with a silver comb. And when she saw Childe Rowland
she stood up and said :

> " God pity ye, poor luckless fool,
>   What have ye here to do ?

> " Hear ye this, my youngest brother,
>   Why didn't ye bide at home ?
> Had you a hundred thousand lives
>   Ye couldn't spare any a one.

> " But sit ye down ; but woe, O, woe,
>   That ever ye were born,
> For come the King of Elfland in,
>   Your fortune is forlorn."

Then they sate down together, and Childe Rowland told her all that he had done, and she told him how their two brothers had reached the Dark Tower, but had been enchanted by the King of Elfland, and lay there entombed as if dead. And then after they had talked a little longer Childe Rowland began to feel hungry from his long travels, and told his sister Burd Ellen how hungry he was and asked for some food, forgetting all about the Warlock Merlin's warning.

Burd Ellen looked at Childe Rowland sadly, and shook her head, but she was under a spell, and could not warn him. So she rose up, and went out, and soon brought back a golden basin full of bread and milk. Childe Rowland was just going to raise it to his lips, when he looked at his sister and remembered why he had come all that way. So he dashed the bowl to the ground, and said : " Not a sup will I swallow, nor a bit will I bite, till Burd Ellen is set free."

Just at that moment they heard the noise of some one approaching, and a loud voice was heard saying :

" Fee, fi, fo, fum,
    I smell the blood of a Christian man,
    Be he dead, be he living, with my brand,
    I'll dash his brains from his brain-pan."

And then the folding-doors of the hall were burst open, and the King of Elfland rushed in.

" Strike then, Bogle, if thou darest," shouted out Childe Rowland, and rushed to meet him with his good brand that never yet did fail. They fought, and they fought, and they fought, till Childe Rowland beat the King of Elfland down on to his knees, and caused him to yield and beg for mercy. "I grant thee mercy," said Childe Rowland, "release my sister from thy spells and raise my brothers to life, and let us all go free, and thou shalt be spared." "I agree," said the Elfin King, and rising up he went to a chest from which he took a phial filled with a blood-red liquor. With this he anointed the ears, eyelids, nostrils, lips, and finger-tips, of the two brothers, and they sprang at once into life, and declared that their souls had been away, but had now returned. The Elfin king then said some words to Burd Ellen, and she was disenchanted, and they all four passed out of the hall, through the long passage, and turned their back on the Dark Tower, never to return again. So they reached home, and the good queen their mother, and Burd Ellen never went round a church widershins again.

Molly Whuppie

ONCE upon a time there was a man and a wife had too many children, and they could not get meat for them, so they took the three youngest and left them in a wood. They travelled and travelled and could see never a house. It began to be dark, and they were hungry. At last they saw a light and made for it; it turned out to be a house. They knocked at the door, and a woman came to it, who said: "What do you want?" They said: "Please let us in and give us something to eat." The woman said: "I can't do that, as my man is a giant, and he would kill you if he comes home." They begged hard. "Let us stop for a little while," said they, "and we will go away before he comes." So she took them in, and set them down before the fire, and gave them milk and bread; but just as they had begun to eat a great knock came to the door, and a dreadful voice said:

> "Fee, fie, fo, fum,
> I smell the blood of some earthly one.

Who have you there wife?" "Eh," said the wife, "it's three poor lassies cold and hungry, and they will go away.

Ye won't touch 'em, man." He said nothing, but ate up a big supper, and ordered them to stay all night. Now he had three lassies of his own, and they were to sleep in the same bed with the three strangers. The youngest of the three strange lassies was called Molly Whuppie, and she was very clever. She noticed that before they went to bed the giant put straw ropes round her neck and her sisters', and round his own lassies' necks he put gold chains. So Molly took care and did not fall asleep, but waited till she was sure every one was sleeping sound. Then she slipped out of the bed, and took the straw ropes off her own and her sisters' necks, and took the gold chains off the giant's lassies. She then put the straw ropes on the giant's lassies and the gold on herself and her sisters, and lay down. And in the middle of the night up rose the giant, armed with a great club, and felt for the necks with the straw. It was dark. He took his own lassies out of bed on to the floor, and battered them until they were dead, and then lay down again, thinking he had managed finely, Molly thought it time she and her sisters were off and away, so she wakened them and told them to be quiet, and they slipped out of the house. They all got out safe, and they ran and ran, and never stopped until morning, when they saw a grand house before them. It turned out to be a king's house : so Molly went in, and told her story to the king. He said : "Well, Molly, you are a clever girl, and you have managed well ; but, if you would manage better, and go back, and steal the giant's sword that hangs on the back of his bed, I would give your eldest sister my eldest son to marry." Molly said she would try. So she went back, and managed to slip into the giant's house, and crept

in below the bed.   The giant came home, and ate up a
great supper, and went to bed.   Molly waited until he was
snoring, and she crept out, and reached over the giant and
got down the sword ; but just as she got it out over the
bed it gave a rattle, and up jumped the giant, and Molly
ran out at the door and the sword with her; and she ran,
and he ran, till they came to the " Bridge of one hair "; and
she got over, but he couldn't, and he says, " Woe worth ye,
Molly Whuppie ! never ye come again."   And she says :
" Twice yet, carle," quoth she, " I'll come to Spain."   So
Molly took the sword to the king, and her sister was
married to his son.

Well, the king he says : " Ye've managed well, Molly ;
but if ye would manage better, and steal the purse that
lies below the giant's pillow, I would marry your second
sister to my second son."   And Molly said she would try.
So she set out for the giant's house, and slipped in, and
hid again below the bed, and waited till the giant had
eaten his supper, and was snoring sound asleep.   She
slipped out, and slipped her hand below the pillow, and
got out the purse; but just as she was going out the giant
wakened, and ran after her ; and she ran, and he ran, till
they came to the " Bridge of one hair," and she got over, but
he couldn't, and he said, " Woe worth ye, Molly Whuppie !
never you come again."   " Once yet, carle," quoth she,
" I'll come to Spain."   So Molly took the purse to the
king, and her second sister was married to the king's
second son.

After that the king says to Molly : " Molly, you are a
clever girl, but if you would do better yet, and steal the
giant's ring that he wears on his finger, I will give you my

youngest son for yourself." Molly said she would **try.**
So back she goes to the giant's house, and hides herself
below the bed. The giant wasn't long ere he came home,
and, after he had eaten a great big supper, he went to his
bed, and shortly was snoring loud. Molly crept out and
reached over the bed, and got hold of the giant's hand, and

she pulled and she pulled until she got off the ring ; but
just as she got it off the giant got up, and gripped her by
the hand, and he says : "Now I have caught you, Molly
Whuppie, and, if I had done as much ill to you as ye
have done to me, what would ye do to me ? "

Molly says : " I would put you into a sack, and I'd put
the cat inside wi' you, and the dog aside you, and a needle
and thread and a shears, and I'd hang you up upon the

wall, and I'd go to the wood, and choose the thickest stick I could get, and I would come home, and take you down, and bang you till you were dead."

"Well, Molly," says the giant, "I'll just do that to you."

So he gets a sack, and puts Molly into it, and the cat and the dog beside her, and a needle and thread and shears, and hangs her up upon the wall, and goes to the wood to choose a stick.

Molly she sings out: "Oh, if ye saw what I see."

"Oh," says the giant's wife, "what do ye see, Molly?"

But Molly never said a word but, "Oh, if ye saw what I see!"

The giant's wife begged that Molly would take her up into the sack till she would see what Molly saw. So Molly took the shears and cut a hole in the sack, and took out the needle and thread with her, and jumped down and helped the giant's wife up into the sack, and sewed up the hole.

The giant's wife saw nothing, and began to ask to get down again; but Molly never minded, but hid herself at the back of the door. Home came the giant, and a great big tree in his hand, and he took down the sack, and began to batter it. His wife cried, "It's me, man;" but the dog barked and the cat mewed, and he did not know his wife's voice. But Molly came out from the back of the door, and the giant saw her, and he after her; and he ran and she ran, till they came to the "Bridge of one hair," and she got over but he couldn't; and he said,

"Woe worth you, Molly Whuppie! never you come again." "Never more, carle," quoth she, "will I come again to Spain."

So Molly took the ring to the king, and she was married to his youngest son, and she never saw the giant again.

The Red Ettin

THERE was once a widow that lived on a small bit of ground, which she rented from a farmer. And she had two sons; and by-and-by it was time for the wife to send them away to seek their fortune. So she told her eldest son one day to take a can and bring her water from the well, that she might bake a cake for him ; and however much or however little water he might bring, the cake would be great or small accordingly, and that cake was to be all that she could give him when he went on his travels.

The lad went away with the can to the well, and filled it with water, and then came away home again ; but the can being broken, the most part of the water had run out before he got back. So his cake was very small ; yet small as it was, his mother asked him if he was willing to take the half of it with her blessing, telling him that, if he chose rather to take the whole, he would only get it with her curse. The young man, thinking he might have to travel a far way, and not knowing when or how he might get other provisions, said he would like to have the whole cake, come of his mother's malison what might ; so she gave him the whole cake, and her malison along with it. Then he took his brother aside, and gave him a knife to keep till he should come back, desiring him to look at it every morning, and as long as it continued to be clear, then he might be sure that the owner of it was well ; but if it grew dim and rusty, then for certain some ill had befallen him.

So the young man went to seek his fortune. And he went all that day, and all the next day ; and on the third day, in the afternoon, he came up to where a shepherd was sitting with a flock of sheep. And he went up to the shepherd and asked him who the sheep belonged to ; and he answered :

> " The Red Ettin of Ireland
>   Once lived in Ballygan,
> And stole King Malcolm's daughter
>   The king of fair Scotland.
> He beats her, he binds her,
>   He lays her on a band ;
> And every day he strikes her
>   With a bright silver wand.
> Like Julïan the Roman,
> He's one that fears no man.
>
> " It's said there's one predestinate
>   To be his mortal foe ;
> But that man is yet unborn,
>   And long may it be so."

This shepherd also told him to beware of the beasts he should next meet, for they were of a very different kind from any he had yet seen.

So the young man went on, and by-and-by he saw a
multitude of very dreadful beasts, with two heads, and on

every head four horns.   And he was sore frightened, and
ran away from them as fast as he could ; and glad was
he when he came to a castle that stood on a hillock, with
the door standing wide open to the wall.   And he went
into the castle for shelter, and there he saw an old wife
sitting beside the kitchen fire.   He asked the wife if he
might stay for the night, as he was tired with a long
journey ; and the wife said he might, but it was not a
good place for him to be in, as it belonged to the Red

Ettin, who was a very terrible beast, with three heads, that spared no living man it could get hold of. The young man would have gone away, but he was afraid of the beasts on the outside of the castle ; so he beseeched the old woman to hide him as best she could, and not tell the Ettin he was there. He thought, if he could put over the night, he might get away in the morning, without meeting with the beasts, and so escape. But he had not been long in his hiding-hole, before the awful Ettin came in ; and no sooner was he in, than he was heard crying :

> " Snouk but and snouk ben,
> I find the smell of an earthly man,
> Be he living, or be he dead,
> His heart this night shall kitchen my bread."

The monster soon found the poor young man, and pulled him from his hole. And when he had got him out, he told him that if he could answer him three questions his life should be spared. So the first head asked : " A thing without an end, what's that ?" But the young man knew not. Then the second head said : " The smaller, the more dangerous, what's that ?" But the young man knew it not. And then the third head asked : "The dead carrying the living ; riddle me that ?" But the young man had to give it up. The lad not being able to answer one of these questions, the Red Ettin took a mallet and knocked him on the head, and turned him into a pillar of stone.

On the morning after this happened, the younger brother took out the knife to look at it, and he was grieved to find it all brown with rust. He told his mother that the time was now come for him to go away

upon his travels also ; so she requested him to take the
can to the well for water, that she might make a cake
for him. And he went, and as he was bringing home
the water, a raven over his head cried to him to look,
and he would see that the water was running out. And
he was a young man of sense, and seeing the water
running out, he took some clay and patched up the
holes, so that he brought home enough water to bake a
large cake. When his mother put it to him to take the
half cake with her blessing, he took it in preference to
having the whole with her malison ; and yet the half
was bigger than what the other lad had got.

So he went away on his journey ; and after he had
travelled a far way, he met with an old woman that
asked him if he would give her a bit of his bannock.
And he said : " I will gladly do that," and so he gave her
a piece of the bannock ; and for that she gave him
a magic wand, that might yet be of service to him, if
he took care to use it rightly. Then the old woman,
who was a fairy, told him a great deal that would happen
to him, and what he ought to do in all circumstances ;
and after that she vanished in an instant out of his sight.
He went on a great way farther, and then he came up
to the old man herding the sheep ; and when he asked
whose sheep these were, the answer was :

"The Red Ettin of Ireland
    Once lived in Ballygan,
And stole King Malcolm's daughter,
    The king of Fair Scotland.

"He beats her, he binds her,
    He lays her on a band ;

And every day he strikes her
With a bright silver wand.
Like Julian the Roman,
He's one that fears no man.

"But now I fear his end is near,
And destiny at hand ;
And you're to be, I plainly see,
The heir of all his land."

When he came to the place where the monstrous
beasts were standing, he did not stop nor run away, but
went boldly through amongst them. One came up
roaring with open mouth to devour him, when he struck
it with his wand, and laid it in an instant dead at his
feet. He soon came to the Ettin's castle, where he
knocked, and was admitted. The old woman who sat
by the fire warned him of the terrible Ettin, and what
had been the fate of his brother ; but he was not to be
daunted. The monster soon came in, saying :

"Snouk but and snouk ben,
I find the smell of an earthly man ;
Be he living, or be he dead,
His heart shall be kitchen to my bread."

He quickly espied the young man, and bade him come
forth on the floor. And then he put the three questions
to him ; but the young man had been told everything
by the good fairy, so he was able to answer all the
questions. So when the first head asked, " What's the
thing without an end ?" he said : " A bowl." And when
the second head said : " The smaller the more dangerous ;
what's that?" he said at once, " A bridge." And last,
the third head said: " When does the dead carry the living,

riddle me that?" Then the young man answered up at once and said: "When a ship sails on the sea with men inside her." When the Ettin found this, he knew that his power was gone. The young man then took up an axe and hewed off the monster's three heads. He next asked the old woman to show him where the king's daughter lay; and the old woman took him upstairs, and opened a great many doors, and out of every door came a beautiful lady who had been imprisoned there by the Ettin; and one of the ladies was the king's daughter. She also took him down into a low room, and there stood a stone pillar, that he had only to touch with his wand, when his brother started into life. And the whole of the prisoners were overjoyed at their deliverance, for which they thanked the young man. Next day they all set out for the king's court, and a gallant company they made. And the king married his daughter to the young man that had delivered her, and gave a noble's daughter to his brother; and so they all lived happily all the rest of their days,

The Golden Arm

THERE was once a man who travelled the land all over in search of a wife. He saw young and old, rich and poor, pretty and plain, and could not meet with one to his mind. At last he found a woman, young, fair, and rich, who possessed a right arm of solid gold. He married her at once, and thought no man so fortunate as he was. They lived happily together, but, though he wished people to think otherwise, he was fonder of the golden arm than of all his wife's gifts besides.

At last she died. The husband put on the blackest black, and pulled the longest face at the funeral ; but for all that he got up in the middle of the night, dug up the body, and cut off the golden arm. He hurried home to hide his treasure, and thought no one would know.

The following night he put the golden arm under his pillow, and was just falling asleep, when the ghost of his dead wife glided into the room. Stalking up to the bedside it drew the curtain, and looked at him reproachfully. Pretending not to be afraid, he spoke to the ghost, and said : " What hast thou done with thy cheeks so red ? '

" All withered and wasted away," replied the ghost, in a hollow tone.

" What hast thou done with thy red rosy lips ? "

" All withered and wasted away."

" What hast thou done with thy golden hair ? "

" All withered and wasted away."

" What hast thou done with thy *Golden Arm* ? "

" THOU HAST IT ! "

The History of Tom Thumb

IN the days of the great Prince Arthur, there lived a mighty magician, called Merlin, the most learned and skilful enchanter the world has ever seen.

This famous magician, who could take any form he pleased, was travelling about as a poor beggar, and being very tired, he stopped at the cottage of a ploughman to rest himself, and asked for some food.

The countryman bade him welcome, and his wife, who was a very good-hearted woman, soon brought him some milk in a wooden bowl, and some coarse brown bread on a platter.

Merlin was much pleased with the kindness of the ploughman and his wife ; but he could not help noticing that though everything was neat and comfortable in the cottage, they seemed both to be very unhappy. He therefore asked them why they were so melancholy, and learned that they were miserable because they had no children.

The poor woman said, with tears in her eyes : " I

should be the happiest creature in the world if I had a son ; although he was no bigger than my husband's thumb, I would be satisfied."

Merlin was so much amused with the idea of a boy no bigger than a man's thumb, that he determined to grant the poor woman's wish. Accordingly, in a short time after, the ploughman's wife had a son, who, wonderful to relate ! was not a bit bigger than his father's thumb.

The queen of the fairies, wishing to see the little fellow, came in at the window while the mother was sitting up in the bed admiring him. The queen kissed the child, and, giving it the name of Tom Thumb, sent for some of the fairies, who dressed her little godson according to her orders ;

> " An oak-leaf hat he had for his crown ;
> His shirt of web by spiders spun ;
> With jacket wove of thistle's down ;
> His trowsers were of feathers done.
> His stockings, of apple-rind, they tie
> With eyelash from his mother's eye :
> His shoes were made of mouse's skin,
> Tann'd with the downy hair within.

Tom never grew any larger than his father's thumb, which was only of ordinary size ; but as he got older he became very cunning and full of tricks. When he was old enough to play with the boys, and had lost all his own cherry-stones, he used to creep into the bags of his playfellows, fill his pockets, and, getting out without their noticing him, would again join in the game.

One day, however, as he was coming out of a bag of cherry-stones, where he had been stealing as usual, the boy to whom it belonged chanced to see him. " Ah, ah! my little Tommy," said the boy, " so I have caught you stealing my cherry-stones at last, and you shall be rewarded for your thievish tricks." On saying this, he drew the string tight round his neck, and gave the bag such a hearty shake, that poor little Tom's legs, thighs, and body were sadly bruised. He roared out with pain, and begged to be let out, promising never to steal again.

A short time afterwards his mother was making a batter-pudding, and Tom, being very anxious to see how it was made, climbed up to the edge of the bowl ; but his foot slipped, and he plumped over head and ears into the batter, without his mother noticing him, who stirred him into the pudding-bag, and put him in the pot to boil.

The batter filled Tom's mouth, and prevented him from crying ; but, on feeling the hot water, he kicked and struggled so much in the pot, that his mother thought that the pudding was bewitched, and, pulling it out of the pot, she threw it outside the door. A poor tinker, who was passing by, lifted up the pudding, and, putting it into his budget, he then walked off. As Tom had now got his mouth cleared of the batter, he then began to cry aloud, which so frightened the tinker that he flung down the pudding and ran away. The pudding being broke to pieces by the fall, Tom crept out covered all over with the batter, and walked home. His mother, who was very sorry to see her darling in such a woful state, put him into a teacup, and soon washed off the batter ; after which she kissed him, and laid him in bed.

Soon after the adventure of the pudding, Tom's mother

went to milk her cow in the meadow, and she took him along with her. As the wind was very high, for fear of being blown away, she tied him to a thistle with a piece of fine thread. The cow soon observed Tom's oak-leaf hat, and liking the appearance of it, took poor Tom and the thistle at one mouthful. While the cow was chewing the thistle Tom was afraid of her great teeth, which threatened to crush him in pieces, and he roared out as loud as he could : " Mother, mother !"

" Where are you, Tommy, my dear Tommy ? " said his mother.

" Here, mother," replied he, " in the red cow's mouth."

His mother began to cry and wring her hands ; but the cow, surprised at the odd noise in her throat, opened her mouth and let Tom drop out. Fortunately his mother caught him in her apron as he was falling to the ground, or he would have been dreadfully hurt. She then put Tom in her bosom and ran home with him.

Tom's father made him a whip of a barley straw to drive the cattle with, and having one day gone into the fields, he slipped a foot and rolled into the furrow. A raven, which was flying over, picked him up, and flew with him over the sea, and there dropped him.

A large fish swallowed Tom the moment he fell into the sea, which was soon after caught, and bought for the table of King Arthur. When they opened the fish in order to cook it, every one was astonished at finding such a little boy, and Tom was quite delighted at being free again. They carried him to the king, who made Tom his dwarf, and he soon grew a great favourite at court; for by his tricks and gambols he not only amused the king

and queen, but also all the Knights of the Round
Table.

It is said that when the king rode out on horseback, he
often took Tom along with him, and if a shower came
on, he used to creep into his majesty's waistcoat-pocket,
where he slept till the rain was over.

King Arthur one day asked Tom about his parents,
wishing to know if they were as small as he was, and
whether they were well off. Tom told the king that his
father and mother were as tall as anybody about the
court, but in rather poor circumstances. On hearing
this, the king carried Tom to his treasury, the place
where he kept all his money, and told him to take
as much money as he could carry home to his parents,
which made the poor little fellow caper with joy. Tom
went immediately to procure a purse, which was made of
a water-bubble, and then returned to the treasury, where
he received a silver threepenny-piece to put into it.

Our little hero had some difficulty in lifting the burden
upon his back; but he at last succeeded in getting it
placed to his mind, and set forward on his journey.
However, without meeting with any accident, and after
resting himself more than a hundred times by the way,
in two days and two nights he reached his father's house
in safety.

Tom had travelled forty-eight hours with a huge silver-
piece on his back, and was almost tired to death, when
his mother ran out to meet him, and carried him into the
house. But he soon returned to Court.

As Tom's clothes had suffered much in the batter-
pudding, and the inside of the fish, his majesty ordered

him a new suit of clothes, and to be mounted as a knight
on a mouse.

Of Butterfly's wings his shirt was made,
   His boots of chicken's hide ;
And by a nimble fairy blade,
Well learnèd in the tailoring trade,
   His clothing was supplied.
A needle dangled by his side ;
A dapper mouse he used to ride,
Thus strutted Tom in stately pride !

It was certainly very diverting to see Tom in this dress
and mounted on the mouse, as he rode out a-hunting with
the king and nobility, who were all ready to expire with
laughter at Tom and his fine prancing charger.

The king was so charmed with his address that he
ordered a little chair to be made, in order that Tom might
sit upon his table, and also a palace of gold, a span high,

with a door an inch wide, to live in. He also gave him a coach, drawn by six small mice.

The queen was so enraged at the honours conferred on Sir Thomas that she resolved to ruin him, and told the king that the little knight had been saucy to her.

The king sent for Tom in great haste, but being fully aware of the danger of royal anger, he crept into an empty snail-shell, where he lay for a long time until he was almost starved with hunger; but at last he ventured to peep out, and seeing a fine large butterfly on the ground, near the place of his concealment, he got close to it and jumping astride on it, was carried up into the air. The butterfly flew with him from tree to tree and from field to field, and at last returned to the court, where the king and nobility all strove to catch him ; but at last poor Tom fell from his seat into a watering-pot, in which he was almost drowned.

When the queen saw him she was in a rage, and said he should be beheaded ; and he was again put into a mouse trap until the time of his execution.

However a cat, observing something alive in the trap, patted it about till the wires broke, and set Thomas at liberty.

The king received Tom again into favour, which he did not live to enjoy, for a large spider one day attacked him ; and although he drew his sword and fought well, yet the spider's poisonous breath at last overcame him.

> He fell dead on the ground where he stood,
> And the spider suck'd every drop of his blood.

King Arthur and his whole court were so sorry at the loss of their little favourite that they went into mourning

and raised a fine white marble monument over his grave
with the following epitaph :

> Here lies Tom Thumb, King Arthur's knight,
> Who died by a spider's cruel bite.
> He was well known in Arthur's court,
> Where he afforded gallant sport ;
> He rode at tilt and tournament,
> And on a mouse a-hunting went.
> Alive he filled the court with mirth ;
> His death to sorrow soon gave birth.
> Wipe, wipe your eyes, and shake your head
> And cry,—Alas ! Tom Thumb is dead !

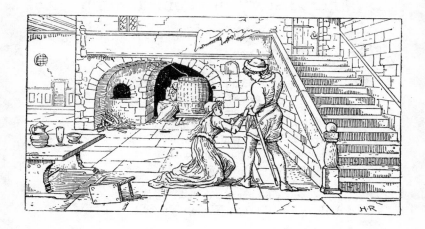

Mr. Fox

LADY Mary was young, and Lady Mary was fair.
She had two brothers, and more lovers than she
could count. But of them all, the bravest and
most gallant, was a Mr. Fox, whom she met when she
was down at her father's country-house. No one knew
who Mr. Fox was; but he was certainly brave, and
surely rich, and of all her lovers, Lady Mary cared for
him alone. At last it was agreed upon between them
that they should be married. Lady Mary asked Mr.
Fox where they should live, and he described to her his
castle, and where it was; but, strange to say, did not ask
her, or her brothers to come and see it.

So one day, near the wedding-day, when her brothers
were out, and Mr. Fox was away for a day or two on
business, as he said, Lady Mary set out for Mr. Fox's
castle. And after many searchings, she came at last to

it, and a fine strong house it was, with high walls and a deep moat. And when she came up to the gateway she saw written on it :

Be bold, be bold.

But as the gate was open, she went through it, and found no one there. So she went up to the doorway, and over it she found written :

Be bold, be bold, but not too bold.

Still she went on, till she came into the hall, and went up the broad stairs till she came to a door in the gallery, over which was written :

Be bold, be bold, but not too bold,
Lest that your heart's blood should run cold.

But Lady Mary was a brave one, she was, and she opened the door, and what do you think she saw ? Why, bodies and skeletons of beautiful young ladies all stained with blood. So Lady Mary thought it was high time to get out of that horrid place, and she closed the door, went through the gallery, and was just going down the stairs, and out of the hall, when who should she see through the window, but Mr. Fox dragging a beautiful young lady along from the gateway to the door. Lady Mary rushed downstairs, and hid herself behind a cask, just in time, as Mr. Fox came in with the poor young lady who seemed to have fainted. Just as he got near Lady Mary, Mr. Fox saw a diamond ring glittering on the finger of the young lady he was dragging, and he tried to pull it off. But it was tightly fixed, and would not come off, so Mr. Fox cursed and swore, and drew his sword, raised it, and brought it down upon the hand of the poor lady. The sword cut off the hand, which jumped up into the air, and fell of all places in the world into Lady Mary's lap. Mr. Fox looked about a bit, but did not think of looking behind the cask, so at last he went on dragging the young lady up the stairs into the Bloody Chamber.

As soon as she heard him pass through the gallery, Lady Mary crept out of the door, down through the gateway, and ran home as fast as she could.

Now it happened that the very next day the marriage contract of Lady Mary and Mr. Fox was to be signed, and there was a splendid breakfast before that. And when Mr. Fox was seated at table opposite Lady Mary, he looked at her. "How pale you are this morning, my dear." "Yes," said she, "I had a bad night's rest last night. I had horrible dreams." "Dreams go by contraries," said Mr. Fox; "but tell us your dream, and your sweet voice will make the time pass till the happy hour comes."

"I dreamed," said Lady Mary, "that I went yestermorn to your castle, and I found it in the woods, with high walls, and a deep moat, and over the gateway was written:

Be bold, be bold.

"But it is not so, nor it was not so," said Mr. Fox.

"And when I came to the doorway over it was written:

Be bold, be bold, but not too bold.

"It is not so, nor it was not so," said Mr. Fox.

"And then I went upstairs, and came to a gallery, at the end of which was a door, on which was written:

Be bold, be bold, but not too bold,
Lest that your heart's blood should run cold.

"It is not so, nor it was not so," said Mr. Fox.

"And then—and then I opened the door, and the room was filled with bodies and skeletons of poor dead women, all stained with their blood."

"It is not so, nor it was not so. And God forbid it should be so," said Mr. Fox.

"I then dreamed that I rushed down the gallery, and just as I was going down the stairs, I saw you, Mr. Fox, coming up to the hall door, dragging after you a poor young lady, rich and beautiful."

"It is not so, nor it was not so. And God forbid it should be so," said Mr. Fox.

"I rushed downstairs, just in time to hide myself behind a cask, when you, Mr. Fox, came in dragging the young lady by the arm. And, as you passed me, Mr. Fox, I thought I saw you try and get off her diamond ring, and when you could not, Mr. Fox, it seemed to me in my dream, that you out with your sword and hacked off the poor lady's hand to get the ring."

"It is not so, nor it was not so. And God forbid it should be so," said Mr. Fox, and was going to say something else as he rose from his seat, when Lady Mary cried out:

"But it is so, and it was so. Here's hand and ring I have to show," and pulled out the lady's hand from her dress, and pointed it straight at Mr. Fox.

At once her brothers and her friends drew their swords and cut Mr. Fox into a thousand pieces.

Lazy Jack

ONCE upon a time there was a boy whose name was Jack, and he lived with his mother on a common. They were very poor, and the old woman got her living by spinning, but Jack was so lazy that he would do nothing but bask in the sun in the hot weather, and sit by the corner of the hearth in the winter-time. So they called him lazy Jack. His

mother could not get him to do anything for her, and at
last told him, one Monday, that if he did not begin to
work for his porridge she would turn him out to get his
living as he could.

This roused Jack, and he went out and hired himself
for the next day to a neighbouring farmer for a penny ;
but as he was coming home, never having had any money
before, he lost it in passing over a brook. " You stupid
boy," said his mother, "you should have put it in your
pocket." " I'll do so another time," replied Jack.

On Wednesday, Jack went out again and hired himself
to a cowkeeper, who gave him a jar of milk for his day's
work. Jack took the jar and put it into the large pocket
of his jacket, spilling it all, long before he got home. " Dear
me !" said the old woman ; "you should have carried it on
your head." " I'll do so another time," said Jack.

So on Thursday, Jack hired himself again to a farmer,
who agreed to give him a cream cheese for his services.
In the evening Jack took the cheese, and went home with
it on his head. By the time he got home the cheese was
all spoilt, part of it being lost, and part matted with his
hair. " You stupid lout," said his mother, "you should
have carried it very carefully in your hands." " I'll do so
another time," replied Jack.

On Friday, Lazy Jack again went out, and hired himself to a baker, who would give him nothing for his work
but a large tom-cat. Jack took the cat, and began carrying it very carefully in his hands, but in a short time
pussy scratched him so much that he was compelled to let
it go. When he got home, his mother said to him, " You
silly fellow, you should have tied it with a string, and

dragged it along after you." "I'll do so another time," said Jack.

So on Saturday, Jack hired himself to a butcher, who rewarded him by the handsome present of a shoulder of mutton. Jack took the mutton, tied it to a string, and trailed it along after him in the dirt, so that by the time he had got home the meat was completely spoilt. His mother was this time quite out of patience with him, for the next day was Sunday, and she was obliged to do with cabbage for her dinner. "You ninney-hammer," said she to her son; "you should have carried it on your shoulder." "I'll do so another time," replied Jack.

On the next Monday, Lazy Jack went once more, and hired himself to a cattle-keeper, who gave him a donkey for his trouble. Jack found it hard to hoist the donkey on his shoulders, but at last he did it, and began walking slowly home with his prize. Now it happened that in the course of his journey there lived a rich man with his only daughter, a beautiful girl, but deaf and dumb. Now she had never laughed in her life, and the doctors said she would never speak till somebody made her laugh. This young lady happened to be looking out of the window when Jack was passing with the donkey on his shoulders, with the legs sticking up in the air, and the sight was so comical and strange that she burst out into a great fit of laughter, and immediately recovered her speech and hearing. Her father was overjoyed, and fulfilled his promise by marrying her to Lazy Jack, who was thus made a rich gentleman. They lived in a large house, and Jack's mother lived with them in great happiness until she died.

Johnny-Cake

ONCE upon a time there was an old man, and an old woman, and a little boy. One morning the old woman made a Johnny-cake, and put it in the oven to bake. "You watch the Johnny-cake while your father and I go out to work in the garden." So the old man and the old woman went out and began to hoe potatoes, and left the little boy to tend the oven. But he didn't watch it all the time, and all of a sudden he heard a noise, and he looked up and the oven door popped open, and out of the oven jumped Johnny-cake, and went rolling along end over end, towards the open door of the house. The little boy ran to shut the door, but Johnny-cake was too quick for him and rolled through the door, down the steps, and out into the road long before the little boy could catch him. The little boy ran after him as fast as he could clip it, crying out to his father and mother, who heard the uproar, and threw down their hoes and gave chase too.   But Johnny-cake outran all three a long way, and was soon out of sight, while they had to sit down, all out of breath, on a bank to rest.

On went Johnny-cake, and by-and-by he came to two well-diggers who looked up from their work and called out : " Where ye going, Johnny-cake ? "

He said : " I've outrun an old man, and an old woman, and a little boy, and I can outrun you too-o-o ! "

" Ye can, can ye ? we'll see about that ? " said they ; and they threw down their picks and ran after him, but couldn't catch up with him, and soon they had to sit down by the roadside to rest.

On ran Johnny-cake, and by-and-by he came to two ditch-diggers who were digging a ditch.   " Where ye going, Johnny-cake ? " said they.   He said : " I've outrun an old man, and an old woman, and a little boy, and two well-diggers, and I can outrun you too-o-o ! "

" Ye can, can ye ? we'll see about that ! " said they ; and they threw down their spades, and ran after him too. Bnt Johnny-cake soon outstripped them also, and seeing they could never catch him, they gave up the chase and sat down to rest.

On went Johnny-cake, and by-and-by he came to a bear.   The bear said : Where are ye going, Johnny-cake ? "

He said : " I've outrun an old man, and an old woman, and a little boy, and two well-diggers, and two ditch-diggers, and I can outrun you too-o-o ! "

"Ye can, can ye?" growled the bear, "we'll see about that!" and trotted as fast as his legs could carry him after Johnny-cake, who never stopped to look behind him.

Before long the bear was left so far behind that he saw he might as well give up the hunt first as last, so he stretched himself out by the roadside to rest.

On went Johnny-cake, and by-and-by he came to a wolf. The wolf said :—

"Where ye going, Johnny-cake?" He said: I've outrun an old man, and an old woman, and a little boy, and two well-diggers, and two ditch-diggers and a bear, and I can outrun you too-o-o!"

"Ye can, can ye?" snarled the wolf, we'll see about that!" And he set into a gallop after Johnny-cake, who went on and on so fast that the wolf too saw there was no hope of overtaking him, and he too lay down to rest.

On went Johnny-cake, and by-and-by he came to a fox that lay quietly in a corner of the fence. The fox called out in a sharp voice, but without getting up: "Where ye going Johnny-cake?"

He said: "I've outrun an old man, and an old woman, and a little boy, and two well-diggers, and two ditch-diggers, a bear, and a wolf, and I can outrun you too-o-o!"

The fox said: "I can't quite hear you, Johnny-cake,

won't you come a little closer ? " turning his head a little
to one side.

Johnny-cake stopped his race for the first time, and
went a little closer, and called out in a very loud voice :
" *I've outrun an old man, and an old woman, and a little
boy, and two well-diggers, and two ditch-diggers, and a bear,
and a wolf, and I can outrun you too-o-o.*"

" Can't quite hear you ; won't you come a *little* closer ? "
said the fox in a feeble voice, as he stretched out his
neck towards Johnny-cake, and put one paw behind his
ear.

Johnny-cake came up close, and leaning towards the
fox screamed out : I'VE OUTRUN AN OLD MAN, AND AN
OLD WOMAN, AND A LITTLE BOY, AND TWO WELL-
DIGGERS, AND TWO DITCH-DIGGERS, AND A BEAR, AND
A WOLF, AND I CAN OUTRUN YOU TOO-O-O ! "

" You can, can you ? " yelped the fox, and he snapped
up the Johnny-cake in his sharp teeth in the twinkling of
an eye.

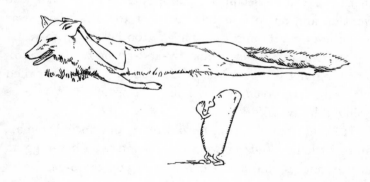

Earl Mar's Daughter

ONE fine summer's day Earl Mar's daughter went into the castle garden, dancing and tripping along. And as she played and sported she would stop from time to time to listen to the music of the birds. After a while as she sat under the shade of a green oak tree she looked up and spied a sprightly dove sitting high up on one of its branches.

She looked up and said : " Coo-my-dove, my dear, come down to me and I will give you a golden cage. I'll take you home and pet you well, as well as any bird of them all." Scarcely had she said these words when the dove flew down from the branch and settled on her shoulder, nestling up against her neck while she smoothed its feathers. Then she took it home to her own room.

The day was done and the night came on and Earl Mar's daughter was thinking of going to sleep when, turning round, she found at her side a handsome young man. She *was* startled, for the door had been locked for hours. But she was a brave girl and said : " What are you doing here, young man, to come and startle me so ? The door was barred these hours ago ; how ever did you come here ?"

" Hush ! hush !" the young man whispered. " I was that cooing dove that you coaxed from off the tree."

" But who are you then ? " she said quite low ; " and how came you to be changed into that dear little bird ? "

" My name is Florentine, and my mother is a queen, ay, and more than a queen, for she knows many a magic spell, and because I would not do as she wished she turned me into a dove by day, but at night her spells lose their power and I become a man again. To-day I crossed the sea and saw you for the first time and I was glad to be a bird that I could come near you. Unless you love me, I shall never be happy more."

" But if I love you," says she, " will you not fly away and leave me one of these fine days ? "

" Never, never," said the prince ; " be my wife and I'll be yours for ever. By day a bird, by night a prince, I will always be by your side."

So they were married in secret and lived happily in the castle and no one knew that every night Coo-my-dove became Prince Florentine. And every year a little son came to them as bonny as bonny could be. But as each son was born Prince Florentine carried the little thing away on his back over the sea to where the queen his mother lived and left the little one with her.

Seven years passed thus and then a great trouble came to them. For the Earl Mar wished to marry his daughter to a noble of high degree who came wooing her. Her father pressed her sore but she said: "Father dear, I do not wish to marry; I can be quite happy with Coo-my-dove here."

Then her father got into a mighty rage and swore a great, great oath, and said: "To-morrow, so sure as I live and eat, I'll twist your bird's neck," and out he stamped from her room.

"Oh, oh!" said Coo-my-dove; "it's time that I was away," and so he jumped upon the window-sill and in a moment was flying away. And he flew and he flew till he was over the deep, deep sea, and yet on he flew till he came to his mother's castle. Now the queen his mother was taking her walk abroad when she saw the pretty dove flying overhead and alighting on the castle walls.

"Here, dancers come and dance your jigs," she called, "and pipers, pipe you well, for here's my own Florentine, come back to me to stay for he's brought no bonny boy with him this time."

"No, mother," said Florentine, "no dancers for me and no minstrels, for my dear wife, the mother of my seven boys, is to be wed to-morrow, and sad's the day for me."

"What can I do, my son?" said the queen, "tell me, and it shall be done if my magic has power to do it."

"Well then, mother dear, turn the twenty-four dancers and pipers into twenty-four grey herons, and let my seven sons become seven white swans, and let me be a goshawk and their leader."

"Alas! alas! my son," she said, "that may not be; my magic reaches not so far. But perhaps my teacher, the spaewife of Ostree, may know better." And away she hurried to the cave of Ostree, and after a while came out as white as white can be and muttering over some burning herbs she brought out of the cave. Suddenly Coo-my-dove changed into a goshawk, and around him flew twenty-four grey herons and above them flew seven cygnets.

Without word or good-bye off they flew over the deep blue sea, which was tossing and moaning. They flew and they flew till they swooped down on Earl Mar's castle just as the wedding party were setting out for the church. First came the men-at-arms and then the bridegroom's friends, and then Earl Mar's men, and then the bridegroom, and lastly, pale and beautiful, Earl Mar's daughter herself. Slowly, slowly they moved to stately music till they came past the trees on which the birds were settling. A word from Prince Florentine, the goshawk, and all rose into the air, herons beneath, cygnets above, and goshawk circling above all. The weddineers wondered at the sight when, swoop! the herons were down among them scattering the men-at-arms. The swanlets took charge of the bride while the goshawk dashed down and tied the bridegroom to a tree. Then the herons gathered themselves together into one feather bed and the

cygnets placed their mother upon them, and suddenly they
all rose in the air bearing the bride away with them in
safety towards Prince Florentine's home.   Surely a wedding party was never so disturbed in this world.   What
could the weddineers do?   They saw their pretty bride

carried away and away till she and the herons and the
swans and the goshawk disappeared, and that very day
Prince Florentine brought Earl Mar's daughter to the
castle of the queen his mother, who took the spell off him
and they lived happy ever afterwards.

Mr. Miacca

TOMMY GRIMES was sometimes a good boy, and sometimes a bad boy; and when he was a bad boy, he was a very bad boy. Now his mother used to say to him: "Tommy, Tommy, be a good boy, and don't go out of the street, or else Mr. Miacca will take you." But still when he was a bad boy he would go out of the street; and one day, sure enough, he had scarcely got round the corner, when Mr. Miacca did catch him and popped him into a bag upside down, and took him off to his house.

When Mr. Miacca got Tommy inside, he pulled him out of the bag and set him down, and felt his arms and legs. "You're rather tough," says he ; "but you're all I've got for supper, and you'll not taste bad boiled. But body o' me, I've forgot the herbs, and it's bitter you'll taste without herbs. Sally! Here, I say, Sally!" and he called Mrs. Miacca.

So Mrs. Miacca came out of another room and said : "What d'ye want, my dear ? "

"Oh, here's a little boy for supper," said Mr. Miacca, "and I've forgot the herbs. Mind him, will ye, while I go for them."

"All right, my love," says Mrs. Miacca, and off he goes.

Then Tommy Grimes said to Mrs. Miacca : "Does Mr. Miacca always have little boys for supper ? "

"Mostly, my dear," said Mrs. Miacca, "if little boys are bad enough, and get in his way."

"And don't you have anything else but boy-meat ? No pudding ? " asked Tommy.

"Ah, I loves pudding," says Mrs. Miacca. "But it's not often the likes of me gets pudding."

"Why, my mother is making a pudding this very day," said Tommy Grimes, "and I am sure she'd give you some, if I ask her. Shall I run and get some ? "

"Now, that's a thoughtful boy," said Mrs. Miacca, "only don't be long and be sure to be back for supper."

So off Tommy peltered, and right glad he was to get off so cheap ; and for many a long day he was as good as good could be, and never went round the corner of the street. But he couldn't always be good ; and one day he went round the corner, and as luck would have it, he hadn't scarcely got round it when Mr. Miacca grabbed him up, popped him in his bag, and took him home.

When he got him there, Mr. Miacca dropped him out ; and when he saw him, he said: "Ah, you're the youngster that served me and my missus such a shabby trick, leaving us without any supper. Well, you shan't do it again. I'll watch over you myself. Here, get under the sofa, and I'll set on it and watch the pot boil for you."

So poor Tommy Grimes had to creep under the sofa, and Mr. Miacca sate on it and waited for the pot to boil. And they waited, and they waited, but still the pot didn't boil, till at last Mr. Miacca got tired of waiting, and he said : " Here, you under there, I'm not going to wait any longer ; put out your leg, and I'll stop your giving us the slip."

So Tommy put out a leg, and Mr. Miacca got a chopper, and chopped it off, and pops it in the pot.

Suddenly he calls out : "Sally, my dear, Sally!" and nobody answered. So he went into the next room to look out for Mrs. Miacca, and while he was there, Tommy crept out from under the sofa and ran out of the door. For it was a leg of the sofa that he had put out.

So Tommy Grimes ran home, and he never went round the corner again till he was old enough to go alone.

Whittington and his Cat

IN the reign of the famous King Edward III. there was a little boy called Dick Whittington, whose father and mother died when he was very young. As poor Dick was not old enough to work, he was very badly off; he got but little for his dinner, and sometimes nothing at all for his breakfast; for the people who lived in the village were very poor indeed, and could not spare him much more than the parings of potatoes, and now and then a hard crust of bread.

Now Dick had heard many, many very strange things about the great city called London; for the country people at that time thought that folks in London were all fine gentlemen and ladies; and that there was singing and music there all day long; and that the streets were all paved with gold.

One day a large waggon and eight horses, all with bells at their heads, drove through the village while Dick was standing by the sign-post. He thought that this waggon must be going to the fine town of London ; so he took courage, and asked the waggoner to let him walk with him by the side of the waggon. As soon as the waggoner heard that poor Dick had no father or mother, and saw by his ragged clothes that he could not be worse off than he was, he told him he might go if he would, so off they set together.

So Dick got safe to London, and was in such a hurry to see the fine streets paved all over with gold, that he did not even stay to thank the kind waggoner ; but ran off as fast as his legs would carry him, through many of the streets, thinking every moment to come to those that were paved with gold ; for Dick had seen a guinea three times in his own little village, and remembered what a deal of money it brought in change ; so he thought he had nothing to do but to take up some little bits of the pavement, and should then have as much money as he could wish for.

Poor Dick ran till he was tired, and had quite forgot his friend the waggoner ; but at last, finding it grow dark, and that every way he turned he saw nothing but dirt instead of gold, he sat down in a dark corner and cried himself to sleep.

Little Dick was all night in the streets ; and next morning, being very hungry, he got up and walked about, and asked everybody he met to give him a halfpenny to keep him from starving ; but nobody stayed to answer him, and only two or three gave him a halfpenny ; so that the poor boy was soon quite weak and faint for the want of victuals.

In this distress he asked charity of several people, and

one of them said crossly : " Go to work for an idle rogue."
" That I will," says Dick, " I will to go work for you, if
you will let me." But the man only cursed at him and
went on.

At last a good-natured looking gentleman saw how
hungry he looked. " Why don't you go to work, my
lad ?" said he to Dick. " That I would, but I do not
know how to get any," answered Dick. " If you are
willing, come along with me," said the gentleman, and
took him to a hay-field, where Dick worked briskly, and
lived merrily till the hay was made.

After this he found himself as badly off as before ; and
being almost starved again, he laid himself down at the
door of Mr. Fitzwarren, a rich merchant. Here he was
soon seen by the cook-maid, who was an ill-tempered
creature, and happened just then to be very busy dressing
dinner for her master and mistress ; so she called out to
poor Dick : " What business have you there, you lazy
rogue ? there is nothing else but beggars ; if you do not
take yourself away, we will see how you will like a
sousing of some dish-water ; I have some here hot enough
to make you jump."

Just at that time Mr. Fitzwarren himself came home
to dinner; and when he saw a dirty ragged boy lying at
the door, he said to him : " Why do you lie there, my
boy ? You seem old enough to work ; I am afraid you
are inclined to be lazy."

" No, indeed, sir," said Dick to him, " that is not the case,
for I would work with all my heart, but I do not know
anybody, and I believe I am very sick for the want of food."

" Poor fellow, get up ; let me see what ails you."

Dick now tried to rise, but was obliged to lie down again, being too weak to stand, for he had not eaten any food for three days, and was no longer able to run about and beg a halfpenny of people in the street. So the kind merchant ordered him to be taken into the house, and have a good dinner given him, and be kept to do what work he was able to do for the cook.

Little Dick would have lived very happy in this good family if it had not been for the ill-natured cook. She used to say : "You are under me, so look sharp ; clean the spit and the dripping-pan, make the fires, wind up the jack, and do all the scullery work nimbly, or——" and she would shake the ladle at him. Besides, she was so fond of basting, that when she had no meat to baste, she would baste poor Dick's head and shoulders with a broom, or anything else that happened to fall in her way. At last her ill-usage of him was told to Alice, Mr. Fitzwarren's daughter, who told the cook she should be turned away if she did not treat him kinder.

The behaviour of the cook was now a little better ; but besides this Dick had another hardship to get over. His bed stood in a garret, where there were so many holes in the floor and the walls that every night he was tormented with rats and mice. A gentleman having given Dick a penny for cleaning his shoes, he thought he would buy a cat with it. The next day he saw a girl with a cat, and asked her, "Will you let me have that cat for a penny?" The girl said : "Yes, that I will, master, though she is an excellent mouser."

Dick hid his cat in the garret, and always took care to carry a part of his dinner to her ; and in a short time he had no more trouble with the rats and mice, but slept quite sound every night.

Soon after this, his master had a ship ready to sail; and as it was the custom that all his servants should have some chance for good fortune as well as himself, he called them all into the parlour and asked them what they would send out.

They all had something that they were willing to venture except poor Dick, who had neither money nor goods, and therefore could send nothing. For this reason he did not come into the parlour with the rest; but Miss Alice guessed what was the matter, and ordered him to be called in. She then said: "I will lay down some money for him, from my own purse;" but her father told her: "This will not do, for it must be something of his own."

When poor Dick heard this, he said: "I have nothing but a cat which I bought for a penny some time since of a little girl."

"Fetch your cat then, my lad," said Mr. Fitzwarren, "and let her go."

Dick went upstairs and brought down poor puss, with tears in his eyes, and gave her to the captain; "For," he said, "I shall now be kept awake all night by the rats and mice." All the company laughed at Dick's odd venture; and Miss Alice, who felt pity for him, gave him some money to buy another cat.

This, and many other marks of kindness shown him by Miss Alice, made the ill-tempered cook jealous of poor Dick, and she began to use him more cruelly than ever, and always made game of him for sending his cat to sea.

She asked him : " Do you think your cat will sell for as much money as would buy a stick to beat you ? "

At last poor Dick could not bear this usage any longer, and he thought he would run away from his place ; so he packed up his few things, and started very early in the morning, on All-hallows Day, the first of November. He walked as far as Holloway ; and there sat down on a stone, which to this day is called "**Whittington's Stone,**" and began to think to himself which road he should take.

While he was thinking what he should do, the Bells of Bow Church, which at that time were only six, began to ring, and their sound seemed to say to him :

"Turn again, Whittington,
Thrice Lord Mayor of London."

" Lord Mayor of London ! " said he to himself. "Why, to be sure, I would put up with almost anything now, to be Lord Mayor of London, and ride in a fine coach, when I grow to be a man ! Well, I will go back, and think nothing of the cuffing and scolding of the old cook, if I am to be Lord Mayor of London at last."

Dick went back, and was lucky enough to get into the house, and set about his work, before the old cook came downstairs.

We must now follow Miss Puss to the coast of Africa. The ship with the cat on board, was a long time at sea ; and was at last driven by the winds on a part of the coast of Barbary, where the only people were the Moors, unknown to the English. The people came in great numbers to see the sailors, because they were of different colour to themselves, and treated them civilly ; and, when they became better acquainted, were very eager to buy the fine things that the ship was loaded with.

When the captain saw this, he sent patterns of the best things he had to the king of the country; who was so much pleased with them, that he sent for the captain to the palace. Here they were placed, as it is the custom of the country, on rich carpets flowered with gold and silver. The king and queen were seated at the upper end of the room; and a number of dishes were brought in for dinner. They had not sat long, when a vast number of rats and mice rushed in, and devoured all the meat in an instant. The captain wondered at this, and asked if these vermin were not unpleasant.

"Oh yes," said they, "very offensive; and the king would give half his treasure to be freed of them, for they not only destroy his dinner, as you see, but they assault him in his chamber, and even in bed, and so that he is obliged to be watched while he is sleeping, for fear of them."

The captain jumped for joy; he remembered poor Whittington and his cat, and told the king he had a creature on board the ship that would despatch all these vermin immediately. The king jumped so high at the joy which the news gave him, that his turban dropped off his head. "Bring this creature to me," says he; "vermin are dreadful in a court, and if she will perform what you say, I will load your ship with gold and jewels in exchange for her."

The captain, who knew his business, took this opportunity to set forth the merits of Miss Puss. He told his majesty: "It is not very convenient to part with her, as, when she is gone, the rats and mice may destroy the goods in the ship—but to oblige your majesty, I will fetch her."

" Run, run ! " said the queen ; " I am impatient to see the dear creature."

Away went the captain to the ship, while another dinner was got ready.   He put Puss under his arm, and arrived at the place just in time to see the table full of rats.   When the cat saw them, she did not wait for bidding, but jumped out of the captain's arms, and in a few minutes laid almost all the rats and mice dead at her feet. The rest of them in their fright scampered away to their holes.

The king was quite charmed to get rid so easily of such plagues, and the queen desired that the creature who had done them so great a kindness might be brought to her, that she might look at her.   Upon which the captain called : " Pussy, pussy, pussy ! " and she came to him.   He then presented her to the queen, who started back, and was afraid to touch a creature who had made such a havoc among the rats and mice.   However, when the captain stroked the cat and called : " Pussy, pussy," the queen also touched her and cried : " Putty, putty," for she had not learned English.   He then put her down on the queen's lap, where she purred and played with her majesty's hand, and then purred herself to sleep.

The king, having seen the exploits of Mrs. Puss, and being informed that her kittens would stock the whole country, and keep it free from rats, bargained with the captain for the whole ship's cargo, and then gave him ten times as much for the cat as all the rest amounted to.

The captain then took leave of the royal party, and

set sail with a fair wind for England, and after a happy voyage arrived safe in London.

One morning, early, Mr. Fitzwarren had just come to his counting-house and seated himself at the desk, to count over the cash, and settle the business for the day, when somebody came tap, tap, at the door. "Who's there?" said Mr. Fitzwarren. "A friend," answered the other; "I come to bring you good news of your ship *Unicorn*." The merchant, bustling up in such a hurry that he forgot his gout, opened the door, and who should he see waiting but the captain and factor, with a cabinet of jewels, and a bill of lading; when he looked at this the merchant lifted up his eyes and thanked Heaven for sending him such a prosperous voyage.

They then told the story of the cat, and showed the rich present that the king and queen had sent for her to poor Dick. As soon as the merchant heard this, he called out to his servants:

"Go send him in, and tell him of his fame;
Pray call him Mr. Whittington by name."

Mr. Fitzwarren now showed himself to be a good man; for when some of his servants said so great a treasure was too much for him, he answered: "God forbid I should deprive him of the value of a single penny, it is his own, and he shall have it to a farthing."

He then sent for Dick, who at that time was scouring pots for the cook, and was quite dirty. He would have excused himself from coming into the counting-house, saying, "The room is swept, and my shoes are dirty and full of hob-nails." But the merchant ordered him to come in.

Mr. Fitzwarren ordered a chair to be set for him, and so he began to think they were making game of him, at the same time said to them : " Do not play tricks with a poor simple boy, but let me go down again, if you please, to my work."

" Indeed, Mr. Whittington," said the merchant, " we are all quite in earnest with you, and I most heartily rejoice in the news that these gentlemen have brought you ; for the captain has sold your cat to the King of Barbary, and brought you in return for her more riches than I possess in the whole world ; and I wish you may long enjoy them ! "

Mr. Fitzwarren then told the men to open the great treasure they had brought with them ; and said : " Mr. Whittington has nothing to do but to put it in some place of safety."

Poor Dick hardly knew how to behave himself for joy. He begged his master to take what part of it he pleased, since he owed it all to his kindness. " No, no," answered Mr. Fitzwarren, " this is all your own ; and I have no doubt but you will use it well."

Dick next asked his mistress, and then Miss Alice, to accept a part of his good fortune ; but they would not, and at the same time told him they felt great joy at his good success. But this poor fellow was too kind-hearted to keep it all to himself ; so he made a present to the captain, the mate, and the rest of Mr. Fitzwarren's servants ; and even to the ill-natured old cook.

After this Mr. Fitzwarren advised him to send for a proper tailor and get himself dressed like a gentleman ; and told him he was welcome to live in his house till he could provide himself with a better.

When Whittington's face was washed, his hair curled, his hat cocked, and he was dressed in a nice suit of clothes he was as handsome and genteel as any young man who visited at Mr. Fitzwarren's ; so that Miss Alice, who had once been so kind to him, and thought of him with pity, now looked upon him as fit to be her sweetheart ; and the more so, no doubt, because Whittington was now always thinking what he could do to oblige her, and making her the prettiest presents that could be.

Mr. Fitzwarren soon saw their love for each other, and proposed to join them in marriage ; and to this they both readily agreed. A day for the wedding was soon fixed ; and they were attended to church by the Lord Mayor, the court of aldermen, the sheriffs, and a great number of the richest merchants in London, whom they afterwards treated with a very rich feast.

History tells us that Mr. Whittington and his lady lived in great splendour, and were very happy. They had several children. He was Sheriff of London, thrice Lord Mayor, and received the honour of knighthood by Henry V.

He entertained this king and his queen at dinner after

his conquest of France so grandly, that the king said: " Never had prince such a subject ; " when Sir Richard heard this, he said ; " Never had subject such a prince."

The figure of Sir Richard Whittington with his cat in his arms, carved in stone, was to be seen till the year 1780 over the archway of the old prison of Newgate, which he built for criminals.

The Strange Visitor

A WOMAN was sitting at her reel one night ;
And still she sat, and still she reeled, and still
she wished for company.

In came a pair of broad broad soles, and sat down at the
fireside ;

And still she sat, and still she reeled, and still she
wished for company.

In came a pair of small small legs, and sat down on the
    broad broad soles ;
And still she sat, and still she reeled, and still she
    wished for company.

In came a pair of thick thick knees, and sat down on the
    small small legs ;
And still she sat, and still she reeled, and still she
    wished for company.

In came a pair of thin thin thighs, and sat down on
    the thick thick knees ;
And still she sat, and still she reeled, and still she
    wished for company.

In came a pair of huge huge hips, and sat down on the
    thin thin thighs ;
And still she sat, and still she reeled, and still she
    wished for company.

In came a wee wee waist, and sat down on the huge huge
    hips ;
And still she sat, and still she reeled, and still she
    wished for company.

In came a pair of broad broad shoulders, and sat down
    on the wee wee waist ;
And still she sat, and still she reeled, and still she
    wished for company.

In came a pair of small small arms, and sat down on the
    broad broad shoulders ;
And still she sat, and still she reeled, and still she
    wished for company.

In came a pair of huge huge hands, and sat down on the small small arms ;
And still she sat, and still she reeled, and still she wished for company.

In came a small small neck, and sat down on the broad broad shoulders ;
And still she sat, and still she reeled, and still she wished for company.

In came a huge huge head, and sat down on the small small neck.

" How did you get such broad broad feet ? " quoth the woman.
" Much tramping, much tramping " (*gruffly*).

" How did you get such small small legs ? "
" *Aih-h-h!*—late—and *wee-e-e*—moul " (*whiningly*).

" How did you get such thick thick knees ? "
" Much praying, much praying " (*piously*).

" How did you get such thin thin thighs ? "
" Aih-h-h !—late—and wee-e-e—moul " (*whiningly*).

" How did you get such big big hips ? "
" Much sitting, much sitting " (*gruffly*).

" How did you get such a wee wee waist ? "
" Aih-h-h !—late—and wee-e-e—moul " (*whiningly*).

" How did you get such broad broad shoulders ? "
" With carrying broom, with carrying broom " (*gruffly*).

" How did you get such small small arms
" Aih-h-h !—late—and wee-e-e—moul " (*whiningly*.)

" How did you get such huge huge hands ? "

" Threshing with an iron flail, threshing with an iron flail"
(*gruffly*).

" How did you get such a small small neck ? "

" Aih-h-h !—late—wee-e-e—moul " (*pitifully*).

" How did you get such a huge huge head ? "

" Much knowledge, much knowledge " (*keenly*).

" What do you come for ? "

" FOR YOU !" (*At the top of the voice, with a wave of the
arm and a stamp of the feet.*)

Childe·Wynd·thrice·kisses·the·
Laidly·Worm·&·rescues·his·Sister
the·Princefs·Margaret·

The Laidly Worm of Spindleston Heugh

IN Bamborough Castle once lived a king who had a fair wife and two children, a son named Childe Wynd and a daughter named Margaret. Childe Wynd went forth to seek his fortune, and soon after he had gone the queen his mother died. The king mourned her long and faithfully, but one day while he was hunting he came across a lady of great beauty, and fell so much in love with her that he determined to marry her. So he sent word home that he was going to bring a new queen to Bamborough Castle.

Princess Margaret was not very glad to hear of her mother's place being taken, but she did not repine, but did her father's bidding, and at the appointed day came down to the castle gate with the keys all ready to hand over to her stepmother. Soon the procession drew near, and the new queen came towards Princess Margaret, who bowed low and handed her the keys of the castle. She stood there with blushing cheeks and eye on ground, and said : " O welcome, father dear, to your halls and bowers, and welcome to you, my new mother, for all that's here is yours," and again she offered the keys. One of the king's knights who had escorted the new queen, cried out in admiration : " Surely this northern Princess is the loveliest of her kind." At that the new queen flushed up and cried out: "At least your courtesy might have excepted me," and then she muttered below her breath : " I'll soon put an end to her beauty."

That same night the queen, who was a noted witch, stole down to a lonely dungeon wherein she did her magic and with spells three times three, and with passes nine times nine she cast Princess Margaret under her spell. And this was her spell :

> I weird ye to be a Laidly Worm,
> And borrowed shall ye never be,
> Until Childe Wynd, the King's own son
> Come to the Heugh and thrice kiss thee ;
> Until the world comes to an end,
> Borrowed shall ye never be.

So Lady Margaret went to bed a beauteous maiden, and rose up a Laidly Worm. And when her maidens came in to dress her in the morning they found coiled up on the bed a dreadful dragon, which uncoiled itself and came towards them. But they ran away shrieking, and the Laidly Worm crawled and crept, and crept and crawled till it reached the Heugh or rock of the Spindlestone, round which it coiled itself, and lay there basking with its terrible snout in the air.

Soon the country round about had reason to know of the Laidly Worm of Spindleston Heugh. For hunger drove the monster out from its cave and it used to devour everything it could come across. So at last they went to a mighty warlock and asked him what they should do. Then he consulted his works and his familiar, and told them: "The Laidly Worm is really the Princess Margaret and it is hunger that drives her forth to do such deeds. Put aside for her seven kine, and each day as the sun goes down, carry every drop of milk they yield to the stone trough at the foot of the Heugh, and the Laidly Worm will trouble the country no longer. But if ye would that she be borrowed to her natural shape, and that she who bespelled her be rightly punished, send over the seas for her brother, Childe Wynd."

All was done as the warlock advised, the Laidly Worm lived on the milk of the seven kine, and the country was troubled no longer. But when Childe Wynd heard the news, he swore a mighty oath to rescue his sister and revenge her on her cruel stepmother. And three-and-thirty of his men took the oath with him. Then they set to work and built a long ship, and its keel they made of the rowan tree. And when all was ready, they out with their oars and pulled sheer for Bamborough Keep.

But as they got near the keep, the stepmother felt by her magic power that something was being wrought against her, so she summoned her familiar imps and said: "Childe Wynd is coming over the seas; he must never land. Raise storms, or bore the hull, but nohow must he touch shore." Then the imps went forth to meet Childe Wynd's ship, but when they got near, they found they had no power over the ship, for its keel was made of

the rowan tree.   So back they came to the queen witch
who knew not what to do.   She ordered her men-at-arms
to resist Childe Wynd if he should land near them, and
by her spells she caused the Laidly Worm to wait by the
entrance of the harbour.

As the ship came near, the Worm unfolded its coils,
and dipping into the sea, caught hold of the ship of Childe
Wynd, and banged it off the shore.   Three times Childe
Wynd urged his men on to row bravely and strong, but
each time the Laidly Worm kept it off the shore.   Then
Childe Wynd ordered the ship to be put about, and the
witch-queen thought he had given up the attempt.   But
instead of that, he only rounded the next point and landed
safe and sound in Budle Creek, and then, with sword
drawn and bow bent, rushed up followed by his men, to
fight the terrible Worm that had kept him from landing.

But the moment Childe Wynd had landed, the witch-
queen's power over the Laidly Worm had gone, and she
went back to her bower all alone, not an imp, nor a man-
at-arms to help her, for she knew her hour was come.
So when Childe Wynd came rushing up to the Laidly
Worm it made no attempt to stop him or hurt him, but
just as he was going to raise his sword to slay it, the voice
of his own sister Margaret came from its jaws saying :

> " O, quit your sword, unbend your bow,
>   And give me kisses three ;
> For though I am a poisonous worm,
>   No harm I'll do to thee."

Childe Wynd stayed his hand, but he did not know what
to think if some witchery were not in it.   Then said the
Laidly Worm again :

"O, quit your sword, unbend your bow,
And give me kisses three,
If I'm not won ere set of sun,
Won never shall I be."

Then Childe Wynd went up to the Laidly Worm and kissed it once ; but no change came over it. Then Childe Wynd kissed it once more ; but yet no change came over it. For a third time he kissed the loathsome thing, and with a hiss and a roar the Laidly Worm reared back and before Childe Wynd stood his sister Margaret. He wrapped his cloak about her, and then went up to the castle with her. When he reached the keep, he went off to the witch queen's bower, and when he saw her, he touched her with a twig of a rowan tree. No sooner had he touched her than she shrivelled up and shrivelled up, till she became a huge ugly toad, with bold staring eyes and a horrible hiss. She croaked and she hissed, and then hopped away down the castle steps, and Childe Wynd took his father's place as king, and they all lived happy afterwards.

But to this day a loathsome toad is seen at times haunting the neighbourhood of Bamborough Keep, and the wicked witch-queen is that Laidly Toad.

The Cat and the Mouse

The cat and the mouse
Play'd in the malt-house :

THE cat bit the mouse's tail off. " Pray, puss, give me my tail." " No," says the cat, " I'll not give you your tail, till you go to the cow, and fetch me some milk."

First she leapt and then she ran,
Till she came to the cow, and thus began :

" Pray, Cow, give me milk, that I may give cat milk, that cat may give me my own tail again." " No," said the cow, " I will give you no milk, till you go to the farmer, and get me some hay."

First she leapt, and then she ran,
Till she came to the farmer and thus began :

" Pray, Farmer, give me hay, that I may give cow hay, that cow may give me milk, that I may give cat milk, that cat may give me my own tail again." " No," says the farmer, " I'll give you no hay, till you go to the butcher and fetch me some meat."

> First she leapt, and then she ran,
> Till she came to the butcher, and thus began :

" Pray, Butcher, give me meat, that I may give farmer meat, that farmer may give me hay, that I may give cow hay, that cow may give me milk, that I may give cat milk, that cat may give me my own tail again." " No," says the butcher, " I'll give you no meat, till you go to the baker and fetch me some bread."

> First she leapt and then she ran,
> Till she came to the baker, and thus began :

" Pray, Baker, give me bread, that I may give butcher bread, that butcher may give me meat, that I may give farmer meat, that farmer may give me hay, that I may give cow hay, that cow may give me milk, that I may give cat milk, that cat may give me my own tail again."

> " Yes," says the baker, " I'll give you some bread,
> But if you eat my meal, I'll cut off your head."

Then the baker gave mouse bread, and mouse gave butcher bread, and butcher gave mouse meat, and mouse gave farmer meat, and farmer gave mouse hay, and mouse gave cow hay, and cow gave mouse milk, and mouse gave cat milk, and cat gave mouse her own tail again !

The Fish and the Ring

ONCE upon a time, there was a mighty baron in the North Countrie who was a great magician and knew everything that would come to pass. So one day, when his little boy was four years old, he looked into the Book of Fate to see what would happen to him. And to his dismay, he found that his son would wed a lowly maid that had just been born in a house under the shadow of York Minster. Now the Baron knew the father of the little girl was very, very poor, and he had five children already. So he called for his horse, and rode into York, and passed by the father's house, and saw him sitting by the door, sad and doleful. So he dismounted and went up to him and said: "What is the matter, my good man?" And the man said: "Well, your honour, the fact is, I've five children already, and now a sixth's come, a little lass, and where to get the bread from to fill their mouths, that's more than I can say."

"Don't be downhearted, my man," said the Baron. "If that's your trouble, I can help you. I'll take away the last little one, and you won't have to bother about her."

"Thank you kindly, sir," said the man ; and he went in and brought out the lass and gave her to the Baron, who mounted his horse and rode away with her. And when he got by the bank of the river Ouse, he threw the little thing into the river, and rode off to his castle.

But the little lass didn't sink ; her clothes kept her up for a time, and she floated, and she floated, till she was cast ashore just in front of a fisherman's hut. There the fisherman found her, and took pity on the poor little thing and took her into his house, and she lived there till she was fifteen years old, and a fine handsome girl.

One day it happened that the Baron went out hunting with some companions along the banks of the River Ouse, and stopped at the fisherman's hut to get a drink, and the girl came out to give it to them. They all noticed her beauty, and one of them said to the Baron : "You can read fates, Baron, whom will she marry, d'ye think ? "

"Oh! that's easy to guess," said the Baron ; "some yokel or other. But I'll cast her horoscope. Come here, girl, and tell me on what day you were born ? "

"I don't know, sir," said the girl, "I was picked up just here after having been brought down by the river about fifteen years ago."

Then the Baron knew who she was, and when they went away, he rode back and said to the girl : "Hark ye, girl, I will make your fortune. Take this letter to my brother in Scarborough, and you will be settled for life." And the girl took the letter and said she would go. Now this was what he had written in the letter :

"DEAR BROTHER,—Take the bearer and put her to death immediately.

"Yours affectionately,

"HUMPHREY."

So soon after the girl set out for Scarborough, and slept for the night at a little inn. Now that **very** night a band of robbers broke into the inn, and searched the girl, who had no money, and only the letter. So they opened this and read it, and thought it **a** shame. The

captain of the robbers took a pen and paper and wrote this letter :

"DEAR BROTHER,—Take the bearer and marry her to my son immediately.

"Yours affectionately,

"HUMPHREY."

And then he gave it to the girl, bidding her begone. So she went on to the Baron's brother at Scarborough, a noble knight, with whom the Baron's son was staying. When she gave the letter to his brother, he gave orders for the wedding to be prepared at once, and they were married that very day.

Soon after, the Baron himself came to his brother's castle, and what was his surprise to find that the very thing he had plotted against had come to pass. But he was not to be put off that way ; and he took out the girl for a walk, as he said, along the cliffs. And when he got her all alone, he took her by the arms, and was going to throw her over. But she begged hard for her life. " I have not done anything," she said : " if you will only spare me, I will do whatever you wish. I will never see you or your son again till you desire it." Then the Baron took off his gold ring and threw it into the sea, saying : " Never let me see your face till you can show me that ring ;" and he let her go.

The poor girl wandered on and on, till at last she came to a great noble's castle, and she asked to have some work given to her ; and they made her the scullion girl of the castle, for she had been used to such work in the fisherman's hut.

Now one day, who should she see coming up to the noble's house but the Baron and his brother and his son, her husband. She didn't know what to do ; but thought they would not see her in the castle kitchen. So she went back to her work with a sigh, and set to cleaning a huge big fish that was to be boiled for their dinner. And, as she was cleaning it, she saw something shine inside it, and what do you think she found ? Why, there was the Baron's ring, the very one he had thrown over the cliff at Scarborough. She was glad indeed to see it, you may be sure. Then she cooked the fish as nicely as she could, and served it up.

Well, when the fish came on the table, the guests liked it so well that they asked the noble who cooked it. He said he didn't know, but called to his servants : " Ho, there, send the cook who cooked that fine fish." So they went down to the kitchen and told the girl she was wanted in the hall. Then she made herself ready and put the Baron's gold ring on her thumb and went up into the hall.

When the banqueters saw such a young and beautiful cook they were surprised. But the Baron was in a tower of a temper, and started up as if he would do her some violence. So the girl went up to him with her hand before her with the ring on it ; and she put it down before him on the table. Then at last the Baron saw that no one could fight against Fate, and he handed her to a seat and announced to all the company that this was his son's true wife ; and he took her and his son home to his castle ; and they all lived as happy as could be ever afterwards.

The Magpie's Nest

Once upon a time when pigs spoke rhyme
And monkeys chewed tobacco,
And hens took snuff to make them tough,
And ducks went quack, quack, quack, O !

ALL the birds of the air came to the magpie and
asked her to teach them how to build nests
For the magpie is the cleverest bird of all at
building nests. So she put all the birds round her and

began to show them how to do it. First of all she took some mud and made a sort of round cake with it.

"Oh, that's how it's done," said the thrush ; and away it flew, and so that's how thrushes build their nests.

Then the magpie took some twigs and arranged them round in the mud.

"Now I know all about it," says the blackbird, and off he flew ; and that's how the blackbirds make their nests to this very day.

Then the magpie put another layer of mud over the twigs.

"Oh that's quite obvious," said the wise owl, and away it flew ; and owls have never made better nests since.

After this the magpie took some twigs and twined them round the outside.

"The very thing !" said the sparrow, and off he went ; so sparrows make rather slovenly nests to this day.

Well, then Madge Magpie took some feathers and stuff and lined the nest very comfortably with it.

"That suits me," cried the starling, and off it flew ; and very comfortable nests have starlings.

So it went on, every bird taking away some knowledge of how to build nests, but none of them waiting to the end. Meanwhile Madge Magpie went on working and working without looking up till the only bird that remained was the turtle-dove, and that hadn't paid any attention all along, but only kept on saying its silly cry : "Take two, Taffy, take two-o-o-o."

At last the magpie heard this just as she was putting a twig across. So she said : "One's enough."

But the turtle-dove kept on saying : "Take two, Taffy, take two-o-o-o."

Then the magpie got angry and said : " One's enough, I tell you."

Still the turtle-dove cried : " Take two, Taffy, take two-o-o-o."

At last, and at last, the magpie looked up and saw nobody near her but the silly turtle-dove, and then she got rarely angry and flew away and refused to tell the birds how to build nests again. And that is why different birds build their nests differently.

Kate Crackernuts

ONCE upon a time there was a king and a queen, as in many lands have been. The king had a daughter, Anne, and the queen had one named Kate, but Anne was far bonnier than the queen's daughter, though they loved one another like real sisters. The queen was jealous of the king's daughter being bonnier than her own, and cast about to spoil her beauty. So she took counsel of the henwife, who told her to send the lassie to her next morning fasting.

So next morning early, the queen said to Anne, " Go, my dear, to the henwife in the glen, and ask her for some eggs." So Anne set out, but as she passed through the kitchen she saw a crust, and she took and munched it as she went along.

When she came to the henwife's she asked for eggs, as she had been told to do ; the henwife said to her, " Lift the lid off that pot there and see." The lassie did so, but nothing happened. " Go home to your minnie and tell her to keep her larder door better locked," said the

henwife. So she went home to the queen and told her
what the henwife had said. The queen knew from this
that the lassie had had something to eat, so watched the
next morning and sent her away fasting; but the princess
saw some country-folk picking peas by the roadside, and
being very kind she spoke to them and took a handful of
the peas, which she eat by the way.

When she came to the henwife's, she said, "Lift the lid
off the pot and you'll see." So Anne lifted the lid but
nothing happened. Then the henwife was rare angry and
said to Anne, "Tell your minnie the pot won't boil if the
fire's away." So Anne went home and told the queen.

The third day the queen goes along with the girl herself to the henwife. Now, this time, when Anne lifted the
lid off the pot, off falls her own pretty head, and on jumps
a sheep's head.

So the queen was now quite satisfied, and went back
home.

Her own daughter, Kate, however, took a fine linen
cloth and wrapped it round her sister's head and took her
by the hand and they both went out to seek their fortune.
They went on, and they went on, and they went on, till
they came to a castle. Kate knocked at the door and
asked for a night's lodging for herself and a sick sister,
They went in and found it was a king's castle, who had
two sons, and one of them was sickening away to death
and no one could find out what ailed him. And the curious
thing was that whoever watched him at night was never
seen any more. So the king had offered a peck of silver to
any one who would stop up with him. Now Katie was a
very brave girl, so she offered to sit up with him.

Till midnight all went well. As twelve o'clock rang, however, the sick prince rose, dressed himself, and slipped downstairs. Kate followed, but he didn't seem to notice her. The prince went to the stable, saddled his horse, called his hound, jumped into the saddle, and Kate leapt lightly up behind him. Away rode the prince and Kate through the greenwood, Kate, as they pass, plucking nuts from the trees and filling her apron with them. They rode on and on till they came to a green hill. The prince here drew bridle and spoke, " Open, open, green hill, and let the young prince in with his horse and his hound," and Kate added, " and his lady him behind."

Immediately the green hill opened and they passed in. The prince entered a magnificent hall, brightly lighted up, and many beautiful fairies surrounded the prince and led him off to the dance. Meanwhile, Kate, without being noticed, hid herself behind the door. There she saw the prince dancing, and dancing, and dancing, till he could dance no longer and fell upon a couch. Then the fairies would fan him till he could rise again and go on dancing.

At last the cock crew, and the prince made all haste to get on horseback ; Kate jumped up behind, and home they rode. When the morning sun rose they came in and found Kate sitting down by the fire and cracking her nuts. Kate said the prince had a good night ; but she would not sit up another night unless she was to get a peck of gold. The second night passed as the first had done. The prince got up at midnight and rode away to the green hill and the fairy ball, and Kate went with him, gathering nuts as they rode through the forest. This time she did not watch the prince, for she knew he would dance, and dance, and dance. But she saw a fairy baby playing with a wand, and overheard one of the fairies say : "Three strokes of that wand would make Kate's sick sister as bonnie as ever she was." So Kate rolled nuts to the fairy

baby, and rolled nuts till the baby toddled after the nuts and let fall the wand, and Kate took it up and put it in her apron. And at cock crow they rode home as before, and the moment Kate got home to her room she rushed and touched Anne three times with the wand, and the nasty sheep's head fell off and she was her own pretty self again. The third night Kate consented to watch, only if she should marry the sick prince. All went on as on the first two nights. This time the fairy baby was playing with a birdie ; Kate heard one of the fairies say : "Three bites of that birdie would make the sick prince as well as ever he was." Kate rolled all the nuts she had to the fairy baby till the birdie was dropped, and Kate put it in her apron.

At cockcrow they set off again, but instead of cracking her nuts as she used to do, this time Kate plucked the feathers off and cooked the birdie. Soon there arose a very savoury smell. "Oh!" said the sick prince, "I wish I had a bite of that birdie," so Kate gave him a bite of the birdie, and he rose up on his elbow. By-and-by he cried out again: "Oh, if I had another bite of that birdie!" so Kate gave him another bite, and he sat up on his bed. Then he said again: "Oh! if I but had a third bite of that birdie!" So Kate gave him a third bite, and he rose hale and strong, dressed himself, and sat down by the fire, and when the folk came in next morning they found Kate and the young prince cracking nuts together. Meanwhile his brother had seen Annie and had fallen in love with her, as everybody did who saw her sweet pretty face. So the sick son married the well sister, and the well son married the sick sister, and they all lived happy and died happy, and never drank out of a dry cappy.

The Cauld Lad of Hilton

AT HILTON HALL, long years ago, there lived, a Brownie that was the contrariest Brownie you ever knew. At night, after the servants had gone to bed, it would turn everything topsy-turvy, put sugar in the salt-cellars, pepper into the beer, and was up to all kinds of pranks. It would throw the chairs down, put tables on their backs, rake out fires, and do as much mischief as could be. But sometimes it would be in a good temper, and then!—"What's a Brownie?" you say. Oh, it's a kind of a sort of a Bogle, but it isn't

so cruel as a Redcap! What! you don't know what's
a Bogle or a Redcap! Ah, me! what's the world
a-coming to? Of course a Brownie is a funny little
thing, half man, half goblin, with pointed ears and hairy
hide. When you bury a treasure, you scatter over it
blood drops of a newly slain kid or lamb, or, better still,
bury the animal with the treasure, and a Brownie will
watch over it for you, and frighten everybody else away.

Where was I? Well, as I was a-saying, the Brownie
at Hilton Hall would play at mischief, but if the servants
laid out for it a bowl of cream, or a knuckle cake spread
with honey, it would clear away things for them, and
make everything tidy in the kitchen. One night, however,
when the servants had stopped up late, they heard a
noise in the kitchen, and, peeping in, saw the Brownie
swinging to and fro on the Jack chain, and saying :

> " Woe's me ! woe's me !
> The acorn's not yet
> Fallen from the tree,
> That's to grow the wood,
> That's to make the cradle,
> That's to rock the bairn,
> That's to grow to the man,
> That's to lay me.
> Woe's me ! woe's me ! "

So they took pity on the poor Brownie, and asked the
nearest henwife what they should do to send it away.
" That's easy enough," said the henwife, and told them that
a Brownie that's paid for its service, in aught that's not
perishable, goes away at once. So they made a cloak of
Lincoln green, with a hood to it, and put it by the hearth

and watched. They saw the Brownie come up, and seeing the hood and cloak, put them on and frisk about, dancing on one leg and saying :

> " I've taken your cloak, I've taken your hood ;
> The Cauld Lad of Hilton will do no more good."

And with that it vanished, and was never seen or heard of afterwards.

The Ass, the Table, and
the Stick

A LAD named Jack was once so unhappy at
home through his father's ill-treatment, that he
made up his mind to run away and seek his
fortune in the wide world.

He ran, and he ran, till he could run no longer, and
then he ran right up against a little old woman who was
gathering sticks. He was too much out of breath to beg
pardon, but the woman was good-natured, and she said he

seemed to be a likely lad, so she would take him to be her servant, and would pay him well. He agreed, for he was very hungry, and she brought him to her house in the wood, where he served her for a twelvemonths and a day. When the year had passed, she called him to her, and said she had good wages for him. So she presented him with an ass out of the stable, and he had but to pull Neddy's ears to make him begin at once to ee—aw! And when he brayed there dropped from his mouth silver sixpences, and halfcrowns, and golden guineas.

The lad was well pleased with the wage he had received, and away he rode till he reached an inn. There he ordered the best of everything, and when the innkeeper refused to serve him without being paid beforehand, the boy went off to the stable, pulled the ass's ears and obtained his pocket full of money. The host had watched all this through a crack in the door, and when night came on he put an ass of his own for the precious Neddy of the poor youth. So Jack without knowing that any change had been made, rode away next morning to his father's house.

Now, I must tell you that near his home dwelt a poor widow with an only daughter. The lad and the maiden were fast friends and trueloves; but when Jack asked his father's leave to marry the girl, "Never till you have the money to keep her," was the reply. "I have that, father," said the lad, and going to the ass he pulled its long ears; well, he pulled, and he pulled, till one of them came off in his hands; but Neddy, though he hee-hawed and he hee-hawed let fall no halfcrowns or guineas. The father picked up a hayfork and beat his son out of the house. I promise you he ran. Ah! he ran and ran till he came bang against the door, and burst it open, and there he was in a joiner's shop. "You're a likely lad," said the joiner; "serve me for a twelvemonths and a day and I will pay you well." So he agreed, and served the carpenter for a year and a day. "Now," said the master, "I will give you your wage;" and he presented him with a table, telling him he had but to say, "Table, be covered," and at once it would be spread with lots to eat and drink.

Jack hitched the table on his back, and away he went with it till he came to the inn. "Well, host," shouted he, "my dinner to-day, and that of the best."

"Very sorry, but there is nothing in the house but ham and eggs."

"Ham and eggs for me!" exclaimed Jack. "I can do better than that.—Come, my table, be covered!"

At once the table was spread with turkey and sausages, roast mutton, potatoes, and greens. The innkeeper opened his eyes, but he said nothing, not he.

That night he fetched down from his attic a table very like that of Jack, and exchanged the two. Jack, none the wiser, next morning hitched the worthless table on to his back and carried it home. "Now, father, may I marry my lass?" he asked.

"Not unless you can keep her," replied the father.

"Look here!" exclaimed Jack. "Father, I have a table which does all my bidding."

"Let me see it," said the old man.

The lad set it in the middle of the room, and bade it be covered; but all in vain, the table remained bare. In a rage, the father caught the warming-pan down from the wall and warmed his son's back with it so that the boy fled howling from the house, and ran and ran till he came to a river and tumbled in. A man picked him out and bade him help him in making a bridge over the river; and how do you think he was doing it. Why, by casting a tree across; so Jack climbed up to the top of the tree and threw his weight on it, so that when the man had rooted the tree up, Jack and the tree-head dropped on the farther bank.

"Thank you," said the man; "and now for what you have done I will pay you;" so saying, he tore a branch from the tree, and fettled it up into a club with his knife. "There," exclaimed he; "take this stick, and when you say to it, 'Up stick and bang him,' it will knock any one down who angers you."

The lad was overjoyed to get this stick—so away he went with it to the inn, and as soon as the innkeeper, appeared, "Up stick and bang him!" was his cry. At the word the cudgel flew from his hand and battered the old fellow on the back, rapped his head, bruised his arms tickled his ribs, till he fell groaning on the floor; still the stick belaboured the prostrate man, nor would Jack call it off till he had got back the stolen ass and table. Then he galloped home on the ass, with the table on his shoulders, and the stick in his hand. When he arrived there he found his father was dead, so he brought his ass into the stable, and pulled its ears till he had filled the manger with money.

It was soon known through the town that Jack had returned rolling in wealth, and accordingly all the girls in the place set their caps at him. " Now," said Jack, " I shall marry the richest lass in the place; so to-morrow do you all come in front of my house with your money in your aprons."

Next morning the street was full of girls with aprons held out, and gold and silver in them ; but Jack's own sweetheart was among them, and she had neither gold nor silver, nought but two copper pennies, that was all she had.

" Stand aside, lass," said Jack to her, speaking roughly. " Thou hast no silver nor gold—stand off from the rest." She obeyed, and the tears ran down her cheeks, and filled her apron with diamonds.

" Up stick and bang them !" exclaimed Jack; whereupon the cudgel leaped up, and running along the line of girls, knocked them all on the heads and left them senseless on the pavement. Jack took all their money and poured it into his truelove's lap. " Now, lass," he exclaimed, " thou art the richest, and I shall marry thee."

Fairy Ointment

D AME GOODY was a nurse that looked after sick people, and minded babies. One night she was woke up at midnight, and when she went downstairs, she saw a strange squinny-eyed, little ugly old fellow, who asked her to come to his wife who was too ill to mind her baby. Dame Goody didn't like the look of the old fellow, but business is business; so she popped on her things, and went down to him. And when she got down to him, he whisked her up on to a large coal-black horse with fiery eyes, that stood at the door; and soon they were going at a rare pace, Dame Goody holding on to the old fellow like grim death.

They rode, and they rode, till at last they stopped

before a cottage door. So they got down and went in and found the good woman abed with the children playing about; and the babe, a fine bouncing boy, beside her.

Dame Goody took the babe, which was as fine a baby boy as you'd wish to see. The mother, when she handed the baby to Dame Goody to mind, gave her a box of ointment, and told her to stroke the baby's eyes with it as soon as it opened them. After a while it began to open its eyes. Dame Goody saw that it had squinny eyes just like its father. So she took the box of ointment and stroked its two eyelids with it. But she couldn't help wondering what it was for, as she had never seen such a thing done before. So she looked to see if the others were looking, and, when they were not noticing, she stroked her own right eyelid with the ointment.

No sooner had she done so, than everything seemed changed about her. The cottage became elegantly furnished. The mother in the bed was a beautiful lady, dressed up in white silk. The little baby was still more beautiful than before, and its clothes were made of a sort of silvery gauze. Its little brothers and sisters around the bed were flat-nosed imps with pointed ears, who made faces at one another, and scratched their polls. Sometimes they would pull the sick lady's ears with their long and hairy paws. In fact, they were up to all kinds of mischief; and Dame Goody knew that she had got into a house of pixies. But she said nothing to nobody, and as soon as the lady was well enough to mind the baby, she asked the old fellow to take her back home. So he came round to the door with the coal-black horse with eyes of fire, and off they went as fast as before, or perhaps a little faster, till they came to Dame Goody's cottage, where the squinny-eyed old fellow lifted her down and left her, thanking her civilly enough, and paying her more than she had ever been paid before for such service.

Now next day happened to be market-day, and as Dame Goody had been away from home, she wanted many things in the house, and trudged off to get them at the market. As she was buying the things she wanted, who should she see but the squinny-eyed old fellow who had taken her on the coal-black horse. And what do you think he was doing ? Why he went about from stall to stall taking up things from each, here some fruit, and there some eggs, and so on ; and no one seemed to take any notice.

Now Dame Goody did not think it her business to interfere, but she thought she ought not to let so good a customer pass without speaking. So she ups to him and bobs a curtsey and said : "Gooden, sir, I hopes as how your good lady and the little one are as well as——"

But she couldn't finish what she was a-saying, for the funny old fellow started back in surprise, and he says to her, says he : "What ! do you see me to-day ?"

"See you," says she, "why, of course I do, as plain as the sun in the skies, and what's more," says she, "I see you are busy too, into the bargain."

"Ah, you see too much," said he ; "now, pray, with which eye do you see all this ?"

"With the right eye to be sure," said she, as proud as can be to find him out.

"The ointment! The ointment!" cried the old pixy
thief. "Take that for meddling with what don't concern
you : you shall see me no more." And with that he
struck her on her right eye, and she couldn't see him any
more ; and, what was worse, she was blind on the right
side from that hour till the day of her death.

The Well of the World's End

ONCE upon a time, and a very good time it was, though it wasn't in my time, nor in your time, nor any one else's time, there was a girl whose mother had died, and her father had married again. And her stepmother hated her because she was more beautiful than herself, and she was very cruel to her. She used to make her do all the servant's work, and never let her have any peace. At last, one day, the stepmother thought to get rid of her altogether; so she handed her a sieve and said to her: "Go, fill it at the Well of the World's End and bring it home to me full, or woe betide you." For she thought she would never be able to find the Well of the World's End, and, if she did, how could she bring home a sieve full of water?

Well, the girl started off, and asked every one she met to tell her where was the Well of the World's End. But nobody knew, and she didn't know what to do, when a queer little old woman, all bent double, told her where it was, and how she could get to it. So she did what the old woman told her, and at last arrived at the Well of the World's End. But when she dipped the sieve in the cold, cold water, it all ran out again. She tried and she tried again, but every time it was the same ; and at last she sate down and cried as if her heart would break.

Suddenly she heard a croaking voice, and she looked up and saw a great frog with goggle eyes looking at her and speaking to her.

"What's the matter, dearie ? " it said.

" Oh, dear, oh dear," she said, "my stepmother has sent me all this long way to fill this sieve with water from the Well of the World's End, and I can't fill it no how at all."

" Well," said the frog, " if you promise me to do whatever I bid you for a whole night long, I'll tell you how to fill it."

So the girl agreed, and then the frog said :

> "Stop it with moss and daub it with clay,
> And then it will carry the water away;"

and then it gave a hop, skip and jump, and went flop into the Well of the World's End.

So the girl looked about for some moss, and lined the bottom of the sieve with it, and over that she put some clay, and then she dipped it once again into the Well of the World's End ; and this time, the water didn't run out, and she turned to go away.

Just then the frog popped up its head out of the Well of the World's End, and said : " Remember your promise."

" All right," said the girl ; for thought she, " what harm can a frog do me ? "

So she went back to her stepmother, and brought the

THE WELL OF THE WORLD'S END.

sieve full of water from the Well of the World's End. The stepmother was angry as angry, but she said nothing at all.

That very evening they heard something tap tapping at the door low down, and a voice cried out :

> " Open the door, my hinny, my heart,
> Open the door, my own darling ;
> Mind you the words that you and I spoke,
> Down in the meadow, at the World's End Well."

" Whatever can that be ? " cried out the stepmother, and the girl had to tell her all about it, and what she had promised the frog.

" Girls must keep their promises," said the stepmother. " Go and open the door this instant." For she was glad the girl would have to obey a nasty frog.

So the girl went and opened the door, and there was the frog from the Well of the World's End. And it hopped, and it hopped, and it jumped, till it reached the girl, and then it said :

> "Lift me to your knee, my hinny, my heart ;
> Lift me to your knee, my own darling ;
> Remember the words you and I spoke,
> Down in the meadow by the World's End Well."

But the girl didn't like to, till her stepmother said : " Lift it up this instant, you hussy ! Girls must keep their promises ! "

So at last she lifted the frog up on to her lap, and it lay there for a time, till at last it said :

> " Give me some supper, my hinny, my heart,
> Give me some supper, my darling ;
> Remember the words you and I spoke,
> In the meadow, by the Well of the World's End."

Well, she didn't mind doing that, so she got it a bowl of milk and bread, and fed it well. And when the frog had finished, it said :

> "Go with me to bed, my hinny, my heart,
>   Go with me to bed, my own darling ;
>   Mind you the words you spake to me,
>   Down by the cold well, so weary."

But that the girl wouldn't do, till her stepmother said : "Do what you promised, girl ; girls must keep their promises. Do what you're bid, or out you go, you and your froggie."

So the girl took the frog with her to bed, and kept it as far away from her as she could. Well, just as the day was beginning to break what should the frog say but :

> "Chop off my head, my hinny, my heart,
>   Chop off my head, my own darling ;
>   Remember the promise you made to me,
>   Down by the cold well so weary."

At first the girl wouldn't, for she thought of what the frog had done for her at the Well of the World's End. But when the frog said the words over again, she went and took an axe and chopped off its head, and lo ! and behold, there stood before her a handsome young prince, who told her that he had been enchanted by a wicked magician, and he could never be unspelled till some girl would do his bidding for a whole night, and chop off his head at the end of it.

The stepmother was surprised indeed when she found the young prince instead of the nasty frog, and she wasn't best pleased, you may be sure, when the prince told her that he was going to marry her stepdaughter because she had unspelled him. But married they were, and went away to live in the castle of the king, his father, and all the stepmother had to console her was, that it was all through her that her stepdaughter was married to a prince.

Master of all Masters

A GIRL once went to the fair to hire herself for servant. At last a funny-looking old gentleman engaged her, and took her home to his house. When she got there, he told her that he had something to teach her, for that in his house he had his own names for things.

He said to her: "What will you call me?"

"Master or mister, or whatever you please sir," says she.

He said: "You must call me 'master of all masters.' And what would you call this?" pointing to his bed.

"Bed or couch, or whatever you please, sir."

"No, that's my 'barnacle.' And what do you call these?" said he pointing to his pantaloons.

"Breeches or trousers, or whatever you please, sir."

"You must call them 'squibs and crackers.' And what would you call her?" pointing to the cat.

"Cat or kit, or whatever you please, sir."

"You must call her 'white-faced simminy.' And this now," showing the fire, "what would you call this?"

"Fire or flame, or whatever you please, sir."

"You must call it 'hot cockalorum,' and what this?" he went on, pointing to the water.

"Water or wet, or whatever you please, sir."

"No, 'pondalorum' is its name. And what do you call all this?" asked he, as he pointed to the house.

"House or cottage, or whatever you please, sir."

"You must call it 'high topper mountain.'"

That very night the servant woke her master up in a fright and said: "Master of all masters, get out of your barnacle and put on your squibs and crackers. For white-faced simminy has got a spark of hot cockalorum on its tail, and unless you get some pondalorum high topper mountain will be all on hot cockalorum" . .

. . . . That's all.

The Three Heads of the Well

LONG before Arthur and the Knights of the Round Table, there reigned in the eastern part of England a king who kept his Court at Colchester. In the midst of all his glory, his queen died, leaving behind her an only daughter, about fifteen years of age who for her beauty and kindness was the wonder of all that knew her. But the king hearing of a lady who had likewise an only daughter, had a mind to marry her for the sake of her riches, though she was old, ugly, hook-nosed, and hump-backed. Her daughter was a yellow dowdy, full of envy and ill-nature; and, in short, was much of the same mould as her mother. But in a few weeks the king, attended by the nobility and gentry, brought his deformed bride to the palace, where the marriage rites were performed. She had not been long in the Court before she set the king against his own beautiful daughter by false reports. The young princess having lost her father's love, grew weary of the Court, and one day, meeting with her father in the garden, she begged him, with tears in her eyes, to let her go and seek her fortune; to which the king consented, and ordered

her mother-in-law to give her what she pleased. She
went to the queen, who gave her a canvas bag of brown
bread and hard cheese, with a bottle of beer. Though
this was but a pitiful dowry for a king's daughter, she took
it, with thanks, and proceeded on her journey, passing
through groves, woods, and valleys, till at length she saw
an old man sitting on a stone at the mouth of a cave, who
said : " Good morrow, fair maiden, whither away so fast ? "

" Aged father," says she, " I am going to seek my
fortune."

" What have you got in your bag and bottle ? "

" In my bag I have got bread and cheese, and in my
bottle good small beer. Would you like to have some ? "

" Yes," said he, " with all my heart."

With that the lady pulled out her provisions, and bade
him eat and welcome. He did so, and gave her many
thanks, and said : " There is a thick thorny hedge before
you, which you cannot get through, but take this wand in
your hand, strike it three times, and say, ' Pray, hedge, let
me come through,' and it will open immediately ; then, a
little further, you will find a well ; sit down on the brink
of it, and there will come up three golden heads, which
will speak; and whatever they require, that do." Promising she would, she took her leave of him. Coming to
the hedge and using the old man's wand, it divided, and
let her through ; then, coming to the well, she had no
sooner sat down than a golden head came up singing :

> " Wash me, and comb me,
> And lay me down softly.
> And lay me on a bank to dry,
> That I may look pretty,
> When somebody passes by."

"Yes," said she, and taking it in her lap combed it with a silver comb, and then placed it upon a primrose bank. Then up came a second and a third head, saying the

same as the former. So she did the same for them, and then, pulling out her provisions, sat down to eat her dinner.

Then said the heads one to another: "What shall we weird for this damsel who has used us so kindly?"

The first said: "I weird her to be so beautiful that she shall charm the most powerful prince in the world."

The second said: "I weird her such a sweet voice as shall far exceed the nightingale."

The third said: "My gift shall be none of the least, as she is a king's daughter, I'll weird her so fortunate that she shall become queen to the greatest prince that reigns."

She then let them down into the well again, and so went on her journey. She had not travelled long before she saw a king hunting in the park with his nobles. She would have avoided him, but the king, having caught a sight of her, approached, and what with her beauty and sweet voice, fell desperately in love with her, and soon induced her to marry him.

This king finding that she was the King of Colchester's daughter, ordered some chariots to be got ready, that he might pay the king, his father-in-law, a visit. The chariot in which the king and queen rode was adorned with rich gems of gold. The king, her father, was at first astonished that his daughter had been so fortunate, till the young king let him know of all that had happened. Great was the joy at Court amongst all, with the exception of the queen and her club-footed daughter, who were ready to burst with envy. The rejoicings, with feasting and dancing continued many days. Then at length they returned home with the dowry her father gave her.

The hump-backed princess, perceiving that her sister had been so lucky in seeking her fortune, wanted to do the same; so she told her mother, and all preparations were made, and she was furnished with rich dresses, and with sugar, almonds, and sweetmeats, in great quantities, and a large bottle of Malaga sack. With these she went the same road as her sister; and coming near the cave, the old man said: "Young woman, whither so fast?"

"What's that to you?" said she.

"Then," said he, "what have you in your bag and bottle?"

She answered : " Good things, which you shall not be troubled with."

" Won't you give me some ? " said he.

" No, not a bit, nor a drop, unless it would choke you."

The old man frowned, saying : " Evil fortune attend ye ! "

Going on, she came to the hedge, through which she espied a gap, and thought to pass through it ; but the hedge closed, and the thorns ran into her flesh, so that it was with great difficulty that she got through. Being now all over blood, she searched for water to wash herself, and, looking round, she saw the well. She sat down on the brink of it, and one of the heads came up, saying : " Wash me, comb me, and lay me down softly," as before, but she banged it with her bottle, saying, " Take that for your washing." So the second and third heads came up, and met with no better treatment than the first. Whereupon the heads consulted among themselves what evils to plague her with for such usage.

The first said : " Let her be struck with leprosy in her face."

The second : " Let her voice be as harsh as a corn-crake's."

The third said : " Let her have for husband but a poor country cobbler."

Well, on she went till she came to a town, and it being market-day, the people looked at her, and, seeing such an ugly face, and hearing such a squeaky voice, all fled but a poor country cobbler. Now he not long before had mended the shoes of an old hermit, who, having no money gave him a box of ointment for the cure of the leprosy, and a bottle of spirits for a harsh voice. So the cobbler having a mind to do an act of charity, was induced to go up to her and ask her who she was.

"I am," said she, "the King of Colchester's daughter-in-law."

"Well," said the cobbler, "if I restore you to your natural complexion, and make a sound cure both in face and voice, will you in reward take me for a husband?"

"Yes, friend," replied she, "with all my heart!"

With this the cobbler applied the remedies, and they made her well in a few weeks; after which they were married, and so set forward for the Court at Colchester. When the queen found that her daughter had married nothing but a poor cobbler, she hanged herself in wrath. The death of the queen so pleased the king, who was glad to get rid of her so soon, that he gave the cobbler a hundred pounds to quit the Court with his lady, and take to a remote part of the kingdom, where he lived many years mending shoes, his wife spinning the thread for him.

Notes and References

THE Fairy Tales of England have been treated in rather a step-motherly fashion. That they once existed in tolerable numbers there are still traces in the library list of Captain Cox, published by the New Shakspere Society, among others, and in odd references in literature and in chap-books. But in the middle of last century the genius of Charles Perrault captivated English and Scotch children with as much force as or, probably, with even more force than he had entranced French ones. Cinderella and Puss in Boots and their companions ousted Childe Rowland and Mr. Fox and Catskin. The superior elegance and clearness of the French tales replaced the rude vigour of the English ones. What Perrault began, the Grimms completed. Tom Tit Tot gave way to Rumpelstiltschen, the Three Sillies to Hansel and Grethel, and the English Fairy Tale became a *mélange confus* of Perrault and the Grimms.

This would not have been so serious if English provincial life had been as conservative and tenacious as the provincial life of France, Italy, or Germany. But railways and the telegraph have disintegrated our provincial life much more than continental. And for various reasons the English peasant has never had so vivid a social life as the *Bauer* or Jacques Bonhomme. Consequently there is less hope of recovering the lost fairy tales of England to such a degree as has been accomplished with such brilliant success in almost every European country during the past thirty years, or still more conspicuously among the Gael of Scotland by the late J. F. Campbell.

Yet something has been done even for England. Halliwell collected a considerable number of folk-tales in two volumes he edited for the Percy Society and reprinted in his *Nursery Rhymes and Tales*. Mr. Baring-Gould appended to the first edition of Henderson's *Folk-Lore of the Northern Counties* (1866) several tales derived from the peasantry of Yorkshire and Devon. More recently Mrs. Balfour collected among the peasants of the Cars in Lincolnshire the remarkable legends and tales she published in *Folk-Lore*, vol. ii., while scattered among the local newspapers and *Notes and Queries,* there have been several drolls reproduced in dialect, among them *Tom Tit Tot* and *Cap o' Rushes,* of this volume, originally published in the Suffolk *Notes and Queries.* Mr. Hartland has collected some of these in his *English Folk and Fairy Tales*, edited for the Camelot Series.

Since the first publication of this book in 1890, Mr. S. O. Addy has published a number of traditional tales collected in the counties of York, Lincoln, Derby, and Nottingham (*Household Tales and other Traditional Romances:* Nutt, 1895). Mr. Baring Gould, who was himself one of the earliest modern collectors of English folk-tales, has brought together a number of legends and tales in his *English Fairy Tales*, 1895, and I have myself published a sequel entitled *More English Fairy Tales*, containing 44 additional stories (Nutt, 1894). This includes a number of previously unpublished English folk-tales collected by Mrs. Balfour and Mrs. Gomme. In the introduction to the notes to this sequel volume, I have made some general remarks on the English folk-tale in particular, and on its relations to the general body of European tales. Of the 87 tales contained in my two volumes, 38 are *Märchen* proper, 10 sagas or legends, 19 drolls, 4 cumulative stories, 6 beast tales, and 10 nonsense stories. With regard to their *provenance*, 8 are derived from ballads, while 29 others show traces of having rhyming portions and thus partaking of the nature of the *cante-fable*. Of the 70 story-radicles common to the European area, about 40 are represented in my two volumes, and of these about 27 are shown in the notes to have been imported. It is probable that of the remaining 30 radicles many once existed in England, and some of them can be traced in the English-speaking pale in Ireland. These statistics show a rather larger proportion of imported tales than in other parts of Europe, where tradition has not so completely died out. But, properly speaking, we may say that from a quarter to a third of the story store of any European country has been derived from abroad, and is in most cases shared by all Europe. Hitherto the attention of folk-lorists has been concentrated on these common elements of European folk-lore, but in reality the chief interest is afforded by the native tales in each country, which are the only ones to which we can legitimately apply the method of "survivals."

In a few cases English folk-tales still exist preserved in metrical form among the Ballads. Thus *Catskin*, which Mr. Burchell told the Primrose children in the *Vicar of Wakefield*, is now only extant as a chapbook ballad. The story of "Binnorie" is closely allied to the theme of *L'os qui chante*, which M. Monseur has, with remarkable industry and success, traced in all the folk-literatures of Europe. Yet in England there is scarcely a trace of its being told otherwise than in ballad form, and that in Lowland Scotch or Northern English.

The folk-literature of the Northern Englishmen known as Scots is clearly closely allied to that of England. The chief collection that has been made of Scotch folk-tales is that of W. Chambers in that delightful book *The Nursery Rhymes of Scotland*, 1842. But out of the twenty-one tales included in the volume sixteen can be traced among Southrons, and till evidence is shown to the contrary, there seems no reason to doubt that the remaining five were also once current on the southern side of the Border. There is no evidence of a distinct story store of Lowland Scots differing from that of Northern or even Southern Englishmen, and I have treated Scots for the purpose of this volume as if they were merely Englishmen, which may Lowland Caledonia forgive!

As some attention has been drawn to this question, I may perhaps explain a little more fully here the principle on which I have acted in making my collection of the folk-tales of the British Isles, which now fill four volumes. My principle of selection has been linguistic rather than ethnographic. I accordingly distinguish two areas in which the folk-tale has passed from mouth to mouth owing to the continuity of language. The first of these includes England and runs up to the Highland line in Scotland. I make no distinction therefore between Lowland Scotch folk-tales, when they existed, from other Northern English tales. As we have seen from the enumeration made in the last paragraph, the stories told by Chambers are of exactly the same character and in most cases of the same plot as those collected in Southern Britain. There is no independent collection of Lowland Scotch tales. I therefore call the stories collected within the English-speaking area English Fairy Tales. Strictly speaking the tales told and collected within the English Pale in Ireland ought perhaps logically to be included under the same title. But in many cases there is evidence that the tales now told in English in East Ireland originally existed in Irish, and belong therefore to the Celtic area of these Isles. I have therefore included them in the two volumes which I have devoted to a selection from the much more luxuriant crop of Celtic fairy tales collected in Scotland and Ireland (*Celtic Fairy Tales*, 1891 ; *More Celtic Fairy Tales*, 1895).

Of the origin of English folk-tales this is not the place to speak at any length. So far as they are common with other European folk-tales, I see no reason for doubting that they all had a common origin. I have given reason in the Introduction to the Notes of my *Indian Fairy Tales* in this series for believing that the source of that international nucleus of the European folk-tales is India. But for each country there remains a residuum peculiar to that country—*e.g.*, for England, *Jack and the Beanstalk* or *Childe Rowland*, and there is no reason to doubt that these are artistic products of the folk-fancy of some Englishman. Whether we can trust to them to obtain archæological evidence of former customs in this island is a somewhat doubtful question, which I have dealt with in a concrete shape in the Notes to *Childe Rowland*.

In the introduction to the notes of the companion volume I have made some remarks on the form taken by the English folk-tale. This is essentially colloquial, and hence rarely if ever rises into romance. This is not peculiar to England. Wherever the stories are collected from the folk they almost always partake of this colloquial and unromantic nature. It would seem as if anything of a romantic type was produced by the folk in the form of ballads rather than of tales. Our idea of fairies is derived from literary versions rather than from those that are really folk-tales. Indeed, we may trace it mainly to the Countess d'Aulnoy and the other French contributors to the *Bibliothèque des fées*, who followed the example of Perrault in giving graceful form to the tales of the folk. In England we get rather humour than romance from the productions of the folk-fancy. Very few of the extant English folk-tales show any signs of constructive plot ability among the folk.

In the present volume there are but few signs of survival of pre-historic custom and belief, which to many folk-lorists form the only source of interest in the folk-tale. I have discussed the chief of these in the note of No. xxi., *Childe Rowland*. But there are traces of transformation in iii., ix., xi., xiii., xxix., xxxiii., xli. Animals or inanimates speak in iii., ix., x., xiv., xvi., xviii., xx., xxii., xxviii., xxxiii., xxxiv., xxxvi., xli., while there are visitants from another world, iii., xv., xxiv., xxxii. Mr. Clodd sees in "Tom Tit Tot" a trace of the curious superstition current among savages that to know a man's name gives you power over him.

In the following notes I give first the *source* whence I obtained the various tales. Then come *parallels* in some fulness for the United Kingdom, but only a single example for foreign countries, with a bibliographical reference where further variants can be found. Finally, a few *remarks* are sometimes added where the tale seems to need it. In two cases (Nos. xvi. and xxi.) I have been more full.

I. TOM TIT TOT.

Source.—Contributed by Mrs. Walter-Thomas (*née* Fison) to the "Suffolk Notes and Queries" of the *Ipswich Journal*, 1877, and reprinted by Mr. E. Clodd in a paper on "The Philosophy of Rumpelstiltskin" in *Folk-Lore Journal*, vii. 138–43. I have reduced the Suffolk dialect.

Parallels.—In Yorkshire this occurs as "Habetrot and Scantlie Mab," in Henderson's *Folk-Lore of Northern Counties*, 221-6 ; in Devonshire as "Duffy and the Devil," in Hunt's *Romances and Drolls of the West of England*, 239-47 ; in Scotland two variants are given by Chambers, *Popular Rhymes of Scotland*, under the title "Whuppity Stourie." The "name-guessing wager" is also found in "Peerifool," printed by Mr. Andrew Lang in *Longmans' Magazine*, July 1889, also *Folk-Lore*, September 1890. It is clearly the same as Grimm's "Rumpelstiltskin" (No. 14) ; for other Continental parallels see Mr. Clodd's article, and Cosquin, *Contes pop. de Lorraine*, i. 269 *seq.*

Remarks.—One of the best folk-tales that have ever been collected, far superior to any of the Continental variants of this tale with which I am acquainted. Mr. Clodd sees in the class of name-guessing stories, a "survival" of the superstition that to know a man's name gives you power over him, for which reason savages object to tell their names. It may be necessary, I find, to explain to the little ones that Tom Tit can only be referred to as "that," because his name is not known till the end.

II. THE THREE SILLIES.

Source.—From *Folk-Lore Journal*, ii. 40-3 ; to which it was communicated by Miss C. Burne.

Parallels.—Prof. Stephens gave a variant from his own memory in *Folk-Lore Record*, iii. 155, as told in Essex at the beginning of the century. Mr. Toulmin Smith gave another version in *The Constitu-*

tional, July 1, 1853, which was translated by his daughter, and contributed to *Mélusine,* t. ii. An Oxfordshire version was given in *Notes and Queries,* April 17, 1852. It occurs also in Ireland, Kennedy, *Fireside Stories,* p. 9. It is Grimm's *Kluge Else,* No. 34, and is spread through the world. Mr. Clouston devotes the seventh chapter of his *Book of Noodles* to the Quest of the Three Noodles.

III. THE ROSE TREE.

Source.—From the first edition of Henderson's *Folk-Lore of Northern Counties,* p. 314, to which it was communicated by the Rev. S. Baring-Gould.

Parallels.—This is better known under the title, "Orange and Lemon," and with the refrain :

> " My mother killed me,
> My father picked my bones,
> My little sister buried me
> Under the marble stones."

I heard this in Australia, and a friend of mine heard it in her youth in Co. Meath, Ireland. Mr. Jones gives part of it in *Folk Tales of the Magyars,* 418–20, and another version occurs in 4 *Notes and Queries,* vi. 496. Mr. I. Gollancz informs me he remembers a version entitled "Pepper, Salt, and Mustard," with the refrain just given. Abroad it is Grimm's "Juniper Tree" (No. 47), where see further parallels. The German rhyme is sung by Margaret in the mad scene of Goethe's "Faust." See Mr. Hartland's *Perseus,* chapter vii., on Death as Transformation.

IV. OLD WOMAN AND PIG.

Source.—Halliwell's *Nursery Rhymes and Tales,* 114.

Parallels.—*Cf.* Miss Burne, *Shropshire Folk-Lore,* 529 ; also No. xxxiv. *infra* ("Cat and Mouse"). It occurs also in Scotch, with the title "The Wife and her Bush of Berries," Chambers's *Pop. Rhymes,* p. 57. Newell, *Games and Songs of American Children,* gives a game named "Club-fist" (No. 75), founded on this, and in his notes refers to German, Danish, and Spanish variants. (*Cf.* Cosquin, ii. 36 *seq.* See also *Celtic Fairy Tales,* notes on "Munachar and Manachar.")

Remarks.—One of the class of Accumulative stories, which are well represented in England. (*Cf. infra*, Nos. xvi., xx., xxxiv., and lxxx. in *More English Fairy Tales*.)

V. HOW JACK SOUGHT HIS FORTUNE.

Source —American Folk-Lore Journal, l., 227-8. I have eliminated a mal-odorous and un-English skunk.

Parallels.—Two other versions are given in the *Journal*, *l. c.* One of these, however, was probably derived from Grimm's "Town Musicians of Bremen" (No. 27). That the others came from the British Isles is shown by the fact that it occurs in Ireland (Kennedy, *Fictions*, pp. 5-10. See *Celtic Fairy Tales*, No. xiv.) and Scotland (Campbell, No. 11). For other variants, see R. Köhler in Gonzenbach, *Sicil. Märchen*, ii. 245.

VI. MR. VINEGAR.

Source.—Halliwell, p. 149. From the West of England.

Parallels.—This is the *Hans im Glück* of Grimm (No. 83). *Cf.*, too, "Lazy Jack," *infra*, No. xxvii. Other variants are given by M. Cosquin, *Contes pop. de Lorraine*, i. 241. On surprising robbers, see preceding tale.

Remarks.—In some of the variants the door is carried, because Mr. Vinegar, or his equivalent, has been told to "mind the door," or he acts on the principle, "he that is master of the door is master of the house." In other stories he makes the foolish exchanges to the entire satisfaction of his wife. (*Cf.* Cosquin, i. 156-7.)

VII. NIX NOUGHT NOTHING.

Source.—From a Scotch tale, "Nicht Nought Nothing," collected by Mr. Andrew Lang in Morayshire, published by him first in *Revue Celtique*, t. iii.; then in his *Custom and Myth*, p. 89; and again in *Folk-Lore*, Sept. 1890. I have changed the name so as to retain the *équivoque* of the giant's reply to the King. I have also inserted the incidents of the flight, mainly from the Pentamerone version, and expanded the conclusion, which is very curtailed and confused in the original. The usual ending of tales of this class contains the "sale of bed" incident, for which see Child, i. 391.

Parallels.—Mr. Lang, in the essay "A Far-travelled Tale" in which he gives the story, mentions several variants of it, including the classical myth of Jason and Medea. An American English variant was read by Mr. Newell before the Folk-lore Congress under the title " Lady Feather Flight." Mr. Newell suggests that Shakespeare's *Tempest* owes something to the main idea of the tale, a warlock's daughter falling in love with his captive and helping him with tasks. A fuller study in Cosquin, *l. c.*, ii. 12–28. For the finger ladder, see Köhler, in *Orient und Occident*, ii. 111. *Cf.* also note on " The Battle of the Birds " in *Celtic Fairy Tales*, and on the tale of the Argonauts in *Wonder Voyages*.

VIII. JACK HANNAFORD.

Source.—Henderson's *Folk-Lore of Northern Counties* (first edition), p. 319. Communicated by the Rev. S. Baring-Gould.

Parallels.—" Pilgrims from Paradise " are enumerated in Clouston's *Book of Noodles*, pp. 205, 214–8. I have also two other English variants in MS., "The Bob-tailed Mare" and "Hereafterthis," the latter of which I have given in *More English Fairy Tales*. See also Cosquin, *l. c.*, i. 239.

IX. BINNORIE.

Source.—From the ballad of the "Twa Sisters o' Binnorie." I have used the longer version in Roberts' *Legendary Ballads*, with one or two touches from Mr. Allingham's shorter and more powerful variant in *The Ballad Book*. A tale is the better for length, a ballad for its curtness. "Sweet pale face" occurs in the original, with all deference to my *Saturday Reviewer*.

Parallels.—The story is clearly that of Grimm's " Singing Bone " (No. 28), where one brother slays the other and buries him under a bush. Years after a shepherd passing by finds a bone under the bush and, blowing through this, hears the bone denounce the murderer. For numerous variants in Ballads and Folk Tales, see Prof. Child's *English and Scotch Ballads* (ed. 1886), i. 125, 493 ; iii. 499 ; and the paper of Prof. Monseur referred to in Notes to the "The Magic Fiddle " in *Indian Fairy Tales*. There is an English version in T. Hughes' *Scouring of the White Horse*.

X. MOUSE AND MOUSER.

Source.—From memory by Lady Burne-Jones.

Parallels.—A fragment is given in Halliwell, 43 ; Chambers' *Popular*

Rhymes has a Scotch version, "The Cattie sits in the Kilnring spinning" (p. 53). The surprise at the end, similar to that in Perrault's "Red Riding Hood," is a frequent device in English folk-tales. (*Cf. infra*, Nos. xii., xxiv., xxix., xxxiii., xli.)

XI. CAP O' RUSHES.

Source.—Contributed by Mrs. Walter-Thomas to "Suffolk Notes and Queries" of the *Ipswich Journal*, published by Mr. Lang in *Longmans' Magazine*, vol. xiii., also in *Folk-Lore*, Sept. 1890.

Parallels.—The beginning recalls *King Lear*. For "loving like salt," see the parallels collected by Cosquin, i. 288 ; and for "ring of recognition" my list of Folk Tale Incidents in *Transactions, Folk-Lore Congress*, 1892, *sub voce*. The whole story is a version of the numerous class of Cinderella stories, the particular variety being the Catskin sub-species analogous to Perrault's *Peau d'Ane*. "Catskin" was told by Mr. Burchell to the young Primroses in *The Vicar of Wakefield*, and has been elaborately studied by the late H. C. Coote, in *Folk-Lore Record*, iii. 1–25. It is only now extant in ballad form, of which "Cap o' Rushes" may be regarded as a prose version. I have given a prose version in *More English Fairy Tales*.

In Miss Roalfe Cox's remarkable collection of variants on the Cinderella type of stories published by the Folklore Society, she has given 26 variants of "Cap o' Rushes" through Italy, Sweden, France, Spain, Portugal, Germany, Corsica, and Belgium. Almost all of these contain the "loving-like salt" episode and the heroine disguise. The essence of the tale as a tale is the same as that of the chief plot of *King Lear*. A father misunderstands the expression of affection given by his youngest daughter and drives her forth. After many adventures, during which she marries a young king or prince, the misunderstanding is cleared up and she is reconciled to her father. Now this is contained in Godfrey of Monmouth, whose account thus becomes the earliest written form of the whole series of Cinderella variants. Mr. Newell, the Hon. Sec. of the American Folklore Society, is accordingly inclined to hold that Godfrey's story is the source of the whole cycle. This seems a rather mechanical method of tracing sources, and he would have to explain by what means Godfrey's account became known to the Corsicans and the Basques, as well as how the loving-like salt incident got introduced. It is much more likely that Godfrey himself only utilised an already existing folk-tale from which perhaps he omitted the loving-like salt incident as unsuitable for his purposes.   There is no sign that Shakespeare was acquainted with the folk-tale in composing his *King Lear*, though curiously enough, as I show later on, he refers in it to another folk-tale (see Notes on *Childe Rowland*). On the other hand it is possible that Shakespeare may have used for his *Tempest* the folk-tale which I have entitled " Nix, Nought, Nothing," for hitherto, no definite source has been discovered for that drama.

XII. TEENY-TINY.

Source.—Halliwell, 148.
Parallels.—Hunt, *Drolls of West of England*, p. 452.

XIII. JACK AND THE BEANSTALK.

Source.—I tell this as it was told me in Australia, somewhere about the year 1860.
Parallels.—There is a chap-book version which is very poor ; it is given by Mr. E. S. Hartland, *English Folk and Fairy Tales* (Camelot Series), p. 35 *seq.*   In this, when Jack arrives at the top of the Beanstalk, he is met by a fairy, who gravely informs him that the ogre had stolen all his possessions from Jack's father. The object of this was to prevent the tale becoming an encouragement to theft !   I have had greater confidence in my young friends, and have deleted the fairy who did not exist in the tale as told to me. For the Beanstalk elsewhere, see Ralston, *Russian Folk Tales*, 293–8. Cosquin has some remarks on magical ascents (i. 14).

XIV. THREE LITTLE PIGS.

Source.—Halliwell, p. 16.
Parallels.—The only known parallels are one from Venice, Bernoni, *Trad. Pop.*, punt. iii. p. 65, given in Crane, *Italian Popular Tales*, p. 267, "The Three Goslings ;" and a negro tale in *Lippincott's Magazine*, December, 1877, p. 753 ("Tiny Pig"). Another English version is given in Mr. Lang's *Green Fairy Book*.
Remarks.—As little pigs do not have hair on their chinny chin-chins, I suspect that they were originally kids, who have. This would bring the tale close to the Grimms' "Wolf and Seven Little Kids,"

(No. 5). In Steele and Temple's "Lambikin" (*Wide-awake Stories*, p. 71), the Lambikin gets inside a Drumikin, and so nearly escapes the jackal. See *Indian Fairy Tales*, No. iii. and Notes.

XV. MASTER AND PUPIL.

Source.—Henderson, *Folk-Lore of Northern Counties*, first edition, p. 343, communicated by the Rev. S. Baring-Gould. The rhymes on the open book have been supplied by Mr. Batten, in whose family, if I understand him rightly, they have been long used for raising the ——; something similar occurs in Halliwell, p. 243, as a riddle rhyme. The mystic signs in Greek are a familiar "counting-out rhyme": these have been studied in a monograph by Mr. H. C. Bolton; he thinks they are "survivals" of incantations. Under the circumstances, it would be perhaps as well if the reader did not read the lines out when alone. One never knows what may happen.

Parallels.—Sorcerers' pupils seem to be generally selected for their stupidity—in folk-tales. Friar Bacon was defrauded of his labour in producing the Brazen Head in a similar way. In one of the legends about Virgil he summoned a number of demons, who would have torn him to pieces if he had not set them at work (J. S. Tunison, *Master Virgil*, Cincinatti, 1888, p. 30). Our story is told of Donald McKay in *Folk-Lore Record*, vi. 153; *cf.* too, " Why the Sea is Salt " in Dasent.

XVI. TITTY MOUSE AND TATTY MOUSE.

Source.—Halliwell, p. 115.

Parallels.—This curious droll is extremely widespread; references are given in Cosquin, i. 204 *seq.*: and Crane, *Italian Popular Tales*, 375-6. As a specimen I may indicate what is implied by such bibliographical references throughout these notes by drawing up a list of the variants of this tale noticed by these two authorities, adding one or two lately printed. Various versions have been discovered in

ENGLAND : Halliwell, *Nursery Rhymes*, p. 115.
SCOTLAND : K. Blind, in *Arch. Rev.* iii. ("Fleakin and Lousikin," in the Shetlands).
FRANCE : *Mélusine*, 1877, col. 424; Sebillot, *Contes, pop. de la Haute Bretagne*, No. 55, *Litterature orale*, p. 232; *Magasin pittoresque*, 1869, p. 82; Cosquin, *Contes pop. de Lorraine*, Nos. 18 and 74.

ITALY : Pitrè, *Novelline popolari siciliane*, No. 134 (translated in Crane, *Ital.*
Pop. Tales, p. 257) ; Imbriani, *La novellaja Fiorentina*, p. 244 ; Bernoni,
Tradizione popolari veneziane, punt. iii. p. 81 ; Gianandrea, *Biblioteca
delle tradizioni popolari marchigiane*, p. 11 ; Papanti, *Novelline popolari
livornesi*, p. 19 ("Vezzino e Madonna Salciccia") ; Finamore, *Trad.
pop. abruzzesi*, p. 244 ; Morosi, *Studi sui Dialetti Greci della Terra
d'Otranto*, p. 75 ; *Giamb. Basile*, 1884, p. 37.

GERMANY : Grimm, *Kinder- und Haus-Märchen*, No. 30 ; Kuhn und Schwarz,
Nord-deutsche Sagen, No. 16.

NORWAY : Asbjörnsen, No. 103 (translated in *Fairy Tales from the Far North*
(H. L. Braekstad), p. 183 ; The Cock who fell into the Brewing Vat.

SPAIN : Maspons, *Cuentos populars catalans*, p. 12 ; Fernan Caballero, *Cuentos
y refrañes populares*, p. 3 (" La Hormiguita ").

PORTUGAL : Coelho, *Contos popolares portuguezes*, No. 1.

ROUMANIA : Kremnitz, *Rumänische Mährchen*, No. 15.

ASIA MINOR : Von Hahn, *Griechische und Albanesische Märchen*, No. 56.

INDIA : Steel and Temple, *Wide-awake Stories*, p. 157 ("The Death and
Burial of Poor Hen-Sparrow ").

Remarks.—These 25 variants of the same jingle scattered over the
world from India to Spain, present the problem of the diffusion of
folk-tales in its simplest form. No one is likely to contend, with Prof.
Müller and Sir George Cox, that we have here the detritus of archaic
Aryan mythology, a parody of a sun-myth. There is little that is
savage and archaic to attract the school of Dr. Tylor, beyond the
speaking powers of animals and inanimates. Yet even Mr. Lang
is not likely to hold that these variants arose by coincidence and
independently in the different parts of the world where they have
been found. The only solution is that the curious succession of
incidents was invented once for all at some definite place and time by
some definite entertainer for children, and spread thence through all
the Old World. In a few instances we can actually trace the passage—
e.g., the Shetland Version was certainly brought over from Hamburg.
Whether the centre of dispersion was India or not, it is impossible to
say, as it might have spread east from Smyrna (Hahn, No. 56).
Benfey (*Einleitung zu Pantschatantra*, i. 190-91) suggests that this
class of accumulative story may be a sort of parody on the Indian
stories, illustrating the moral, " what great events from small occasions
rise ! " Thus, a drop of honey falls on the ground ; a fly goes after it,
a bird snaps at the fly, a dog goes for the bird, another dog goes for
the first, the masters of the two dogs—who happen to be kings—
quarrel and go to war, whole provinces are devastated, and all for a
drop of honey ! " Titty Mouse and Tatty Mouse" also ends in a

universal calamity which seems to arise from a cause of no great importance. Benfey's suggestion is certainly ingenious, but perhaps too ingenious to be true.

XVII. JACK AND HIS SNUFF-BOX.

Source.—Mr. F. Hindes Groome, *In Gipsy Tents*, p. 201 *seq.* I have eliminated a superfluous Gipsy who makes her appearance toward the end of a tale *à propos des bottes*, but otherwise have left the tale unaltered as one of the few English Folk-tales that have been taken down from the mouths of the peasantry : this applies also to i., ii., xi.

Parallels.—There is a magic snuff-box with a friendly power in it in Kennedy's *Fictions of the Irish Celts*, p. 49. The choice between a small cake with a blessing, &c., is frequent (*cf.* No. xxiii.), but the closest parallel to the whole story, including the mice, is afforded by a tale in Carnoy and Nicolaides' *Traditions populaires de l'Asie Mineure*, which is translated as the first tale in Mr. Lang's *Blue Fairy Book*. There is much in both that is similar to Aladdin, I beg his pardon, Allah-ed-din ; in Grey Norris *F. L. J.*, i. 316, also in "Penny Jack," a story given by Mr. W. A. Clouston in *Folk-Lore*, No. iv., and in "The Charmed Ring" of *Indian Fairy Tales*.

XVIII. THE THREE BEARS.

Source.—*Verbatim et literatim* from South ·, *The Doctor*, &c., quarto edition, p. 327.

Parallels.—None in full, though not invented by Southey. There is an Italian translation, *I tre Orsi*, Turin, 1868, and it would be curious to see if the tale ever acclimatises itself in Italy. But the incident of sitting in the chairs, &c., is in the Grimms' "*Schneewitchen.*"

Remarks.—"The Three Bears" is the only example I know of where a tale that can be definitely traced to a specific author has become a folk-tale. Not alone is this so, but the folk has developed the tale in a curious and instructive way, by substituting a pretty little girl with golden locks for the naughty old woman. In Southey's version there is nothing of little Silverhair as the heroine : she seems to have been introduced in a metrical version by G. N., much be-praised by Southey. Silverhair seems to have become a favourite, and in Mrs. Valentine's version of "The Three Bears," in "The Old, Old Fairy

Tales," the visit to the bear house is only the preliminary to a long
succession of adventures of the pretty little girl, of which there is no
trace in the original (and this in " The Old, Old Fairy Tales." Oh !
Mrs. Valentine !) I have, though somewhat reluctantly, cast back to
the original form. After all, as Prof. Dowden remarks, Southey's
memory is kept alive more by " The Three Bears " than anything
else, and the text of such a nursery classic should be retained in all its
purity.

Since the first publication of this book I have come across what
appears to be the source from which Southey got the story of " The
Three Bears," though it still remains true that the popularity of the
story among English children is due to Southey. I have published
this interesting version in *More English Fairy Tales* under the title
of " Scrapefoot," in which the Old Woman appears as a Fox, so that
the story is entirely a beast tale. Now there is found to exist among
all countries of Europe a number of tales relating to the feud between
the Fox and the Bear (or Wolf). These stories were worked up by a
mediæval artist into the Beast Epic known as " Reynard the Fox."
It is probable therefore that " Scrapefoot," the original of Southey's
" Three Bears " is a survival of the English form of the Beast Epic.
Altogether Southey's tale affords an extremely interesting example of
the modifications which a story of this kind can undergo. As we
have seen above, it has already been developed from its original form
in Southey's book by popular tale writers who correspond nowadays
to the bards of earlier times. And from the discovery of " Scrapefoot " we learn that Southey changed the fox (or vixen) of the original
into an old woman, and thus disguised its representative character as
the last survival of the Reynard cycle in English folk-tradition.

XIX. JACK THE GIANT-KILLER.

Source.—From two chap-books at the British Museum (London, 1805,
Paisley, 1814 ?). I have taken some hints from " Felix Summerly's "
(Sir Henry Cole's) version, 1845. From the latter part, I have
removed the incident of the Giant dragging the lady along by her
hair.

Parallels.—The chap-book of " Jack the Giant-Killer " is a curious
jumble. The second part, as in most chap-books, is a weak and late
invention of the enemy, and is not *volkstümlich* at all. The first part
is compounded of a comic and a serious theme. The first is that of

the Valiant Tailor (Grimm, No. 20) ; to this belong the incidents of the fleabite blows (for variants of which see Köhler in *Jahrb. rom. eng. Phil.*, viii. 252) and that of the slit paunch (*cf.* Cosquin, *l.c.*, ii. 51). The Thankful Dead episode, where the hero is assisted by the soul of a person whom he has caused to be buried, is found as early as the *Cento novelle antiche;* and Straparola, xi. 2. It has been best studied by Köhler in *Germania*, iii. 199-209 (*cf.* Cosquin, i. 214-5 ; ii. 14 and note ; and Crane, *Ital. Pop. Tales*, 350, note 12). It occurs also in the curious play of Peele's *The Old Wives' Tale*, in which one of the characters is the Ghost of Jack. Fielding refers to Jack the Giant-Killer in the beginning of *Joseph Andrews*. Practically the same story as this part of Jack the Giant-Killer occurs in Kennedy, *Fictions of the Irish Celts*, p. 32, "Jack the Master and Jack the Servant"; and Kennedy adds (p. 38), "In some versions Jack the Servant is the spirit of the buried man."

This incident of the Faithful Dead was also the subject of a Middle English verse romance entitled *Sir Amadace*, an edition of which was produced by the late Prof. George Stephens of Copenhagen in the year 1854 with an introduction which gives some of the folk-lore parallels. The necessity of burial for "laying" the spirit of a dead man runs throughout all primitive thought, and is at the root of most burial customs. It forms the central *motif* of the *Antigone* of Sophocles, and has not been without its influence on Christian theology.

Jack's invisibility recalls the Invisible Helmet which enabled Perseus to fulfil the tasks laid upon him. Upon this see Köhler in *Jahrbuch*, vii. 146, and in Kreutzwald, *Estnische Mährchen*, 359 ; also Steele and Temple's *Wide Awake Stories*, 423. These gifts of magic armour cannot be regarded as primitive ; they must at least be posterior to the Neolithic Age.

The "Fee-fi-fo-fum" formula is common to all English stories of giants and ogres ; it also occurs in Peele's play and in *King Lear* (see note on "Childe Rowland"). Messrs. Jones and Kropf have some remarks on it in their "Magyar Tales," pp. 340-1 ; so has Mr. Lang in his "Perrault," p. lxiii, where he traces it to the Furies in Æschylus' *Eumenides*.

XX. HENNY-PENNY.

Source.—I give this as it was told to me in Australia in 1860. The fun consists in the avoidance of all pronouns, which results in jaw-

breaking sentences almost equal to the celebrated " She stood at the
door of the fish-sauce shop, welcoming him in."

Parallels.—Hallewell, p. 151, has the same with the title "Chicken-
Licken." It occurs also in Chambers's *Popular Rhymes*, p. 59, with
the same names of the *dramatis personæ* as my version. Kennedy,
Fireside Tales of Ireland, p. 25, has it under the title " The End of the
World." For European parallels, see Crane, *Ital. Pop. Tales*, 377, and
authorities there quoted.

XXI. CHILDE ROWLAND.

Source.—Jamieson's *Illustrations of Northern Antiquities*, 1814,
p. 397 *seq.*, who gives it as told by a tailor in his youth, *c.* 1770,
I have Anglicised the Scotticisms, eliminated an unnecessary ox-herd
and swine-herd, who lose their heads for directing the Childe,
and I have called the Erikönig's lair the Dark Tower on the strength
of the description and of Shakespeare's reference. I have likewise
suggested a reason why Burd Ellen fell into his power, chiefly in
order to introduce a definition of "widershins." " All the rest is the
original horse," even including the erroneous description of the
youngest son as the Childe or heir (*cf.* " Childe Harold" and Childe
Wynd, *infra*, No. xxxiii.) unless this is some "survival" of Junior
Right or " Borough English," the archaic custom of letting the heirship
pass to the youngest son. I should add that, on the strength of the
reference to Merlin, Jamieson calls Childe Rowland's mother, Queen
Guinevere, and introduces references to King Arthur and his Court.
But as he confesses that these are his own improvements on the
tailor's narrative I have eliminated them. Since the first appearance of this book, I should add, Mr. Grant Allen has made an ingenious
use of *Childe Rowland* in one of his short stories now collected in the
volume entitled *Ivan Greet's Masterpiece.*

Parallels.—The search for the Dark Tower is similar to that of
the Red Ettin (*cf.* Köhler on Gonzenbach, ii. 222). The formula
" Youngest best," in which the youngest of the three brothers succeeds
after the others have failed, is one of the most familiar in folk-tales,
amusingly parodied by Mr. Lang in his *Prince Prigio*. The
taboo against taking food in the underworld occurs in the myth
of Proserpine, and is also frequent in folk-tales (Child, i. 322). But
the folk-tale parallels to our tale fade into insignificance before its
brilliant literary relationships. Browning has a poem under the title

working upon a line of *King Lear*. There can be little doubt that Edgar, in his mad scene in *King Lear*, is alluding to our tale when he breaks into the lines :

> " Childe Rowland to the Dark Tower came . . . .
> His word was still : ' Fie, foh and fum,
> I smell the blood of a British* man.' "

King Lear, act iii. sc. 4, *ad fin.*

The latter reference is to the cry of the King of Elfland. That some such story was current in England in Shakespeare's time is proved by that curious *mélange* of nursery tales, Peele's *The Old Wives' Tale*. The main plot of this is the search of two brothers, Calypha and Thelea, for a lost sister, Delia, who had been bespelled by a sorcerer, Sacrapant (the names are taken from the " Orlando Furioso "). They are instructed by an old man (like Merlin in " Childe Rowland ") how to rescue their sister, and ultimately succeed. The play has besides this the themes of the Thankful Dead, the Three Heads of the Well (which see), the Life Index, and a transformation, so that it is not to be wondered at if some of the traits of " Childe Rowland " are observed in it, especially as the title explains that it was made up of folk-tales.

But a still closer parallel is afforded by Milton's *Comus*. Here again we have two brothers in search of a sister, who has got into the power of an enchanter. But besides this, there is the refusal of the heroine to touch the enchanted food, just as Childe Rowland finally refuses. And ultimately the bespelled heroine is liberated by a liquid, which is applied to *lips and finger tips*, just as Childe Rowland's brothers are unspelled by applying a liquid to their ears, eyelids, nostrils, lips, and finger-tips. There may be here a trace of the supreme unction of the Catholic Church. Such a minute resemblance as this cannot be accidental, and it is therefore probable that Milton used the original form of " Childe Rowland," or some variant of it, as heard in his youth, and adapted it to the purposes of the masque at Ludlow Castle, and of his allegory. Certainly no other folk-tale in the world can claim so distinguished an offspring.

Remarks.—Distinguished as " Childe Rowland " will be henceforth

---

* " British " for " English." This is one of the points that settle the date of the play ; James I. was declared King of Great *Britain*, October 1604. I may add that Motherwell in his *Minstrelsy*, p. xiv., note, testifies that the story was still extant in the nursery at the time he wrote (1828).

as the origin of *Comus*, if my affiliation be accepted, it has even more remarkable points of interest, both in form and matter, for the folk-lorist, unless I am much mistaken. I will therefore touch upon these points, reserving a more detailed examination for another occasion.

First, as to the form of the narrative. This begins with verse, then turns to prose, and throughout drops again at intervals into poetry in a friendly way like Mr. Wegg. Now this is a form of writing not unknown in other branches of literature, the *cante-fable*, of which "Aucassin et Nicolete" is the most distinguished example. Nor is the *cante-fable* confined to France. Many of the heroic verses of the Arabs contained in the *Hamâsa* would be unintelligible without accompanying narrative, which is nowadays preserved in the commentary. The verses imbedded in the *Arabian Nights* give them something of the character of a *cante-fable*, and the same may be said of the Indian and Persian story-books, though the verse is usually of a sententious and moral kind, as in the *gâthas* of the Buddhist Jatakas. Even in remote Zanzibar, Mr. Lang notes, the folk-tales are told as *cante-fables*. The contemporary Indian story-tellers, Mr. Hartland notes, also commingle verse and prose. There are even traces in the Old Testament of such screeds of verse amid the prose narrative, as in the story of Lamech or that of Balaam. All this suggests that this is a very early and common form of narrative. (*Cf.* note on "Connla" in *Celtic Fairy Tales*.)

Among folk-tales there are still many traces of the *cante-fable*. Thus, in Grimm's collection, verses occur in Nos. 1, 5, 11, 12, 13, 15, 19, 21, 24, 28, 30, 36, 38a, b, 39a, 40, 45, 46, 47, out of the first fifty tales, 36 per cent. Of Chambers's twenty-one folk-tales, in the *Popular Rhymes of Scotland* only five are without interspersed verses. Of the forty-three tales contained in this volume, three (ix., xxix., xxxiii.) are derived from ballads, and do not therefore count in the present connection. Of the remaining forty, i., iii., vii., xvi., xix., xxi., xxiii., xxv., xxxi., xxxv., xxxviii., xli. (made up from verses), xliii., contain rhymed lines, while xiv., xxii., xxvi., and xxxvii., contain "survivals" of rhymes ("let me come in—chinny chin-chin"; "once again . . . . come to Spain"; "it is not so—should be so"; "and his lady, him behind"); and x. and xxxii. are rhythmical if not rhyming. As most of the remainder are drolls, which have probably a different origin, there seems to be great probability that originally all folk-tales of a serious character were interspersed with rhyme, and took therefore the form of the *cante-fable*. It is indeed unlikely that the ballad itself began as continuous verse, and the *cante-fable* is probably the protoplasm out of which both ballad and folk-tale have been differentiated, the ballad by omitting the narrative prose, the folk-tale by expanding it. In " Childe Rowland " we have the nearest example to such protoplasm, and it is not difficult to see how it could have been shortened into a ballad or reduced to a prose folk-tale pure and simple.

The subject-matter of " Childe Rowland " has also claims on our attention, especially with regard to recent views on the true nature and origin of elves, trolls, and fairies. I refer to the work of Mr. D. MacRitchie, " The Testimony of Tradition " (Kegan Paul, Trench, Trübner & Co., 1889)—*i.e.*, of tradition about the fairies and the rest. Briefly put, Mr. MacRitchie's view is, that the elves, trolls, and fairies represented in popular tradition are really the mound-dwellers, whose remains have been discovered in some abundance in the form of green hillocks, which have been artificially raised over a long and low passage leading to a central chamber open to the sky. Mr. MacRitchie shows that in several instances traditions about trolls or " good people " have attached themselves to mounds, which have afterwards, on investigation, turned out to be evidently the former residence of men of smaller build than the mortals of to-day. He goes on further to identify these with the Picts—fairies are called " Pechs " in Scotland—and other early races, but with these ethnological equations we need not much concern ourselves. It is otherwise with the mound-traditions and their relation, if not to fairy tales in general, to tales *about* fairies, trolls, elves, &c. These are very few in number, and generally bear the character of anecdotes The fairies, &c., steal a child, they help a wanderer to a drink and then disappear into a green hill, they help cottagers with their work at night, but disappear if their presence is noticed ; human midwives are asked to help fairy mothers, fairy maidens marry ordinary men or girls marry and live with fairy husbands. All such things may have happened and bear no such *à priori* marks of impossibility as speaking animals, flying through the air, and similar incidents of the folk-tale pure and simple. If, as archæologists tell us, there was once a race of men in Northern Europe, very short and hairy, that dwelt in underground chambers artificially concealed by green hillocks, it does not seem unlikely that odd survivors of the race should have lived on after they had been conquered and nearly exterminated by Aryan invaders and should occasionally have performed something like the pranks told of fairies and trolls.

Certainly the description of the Dark Tower of the King of Elfland in " Childe Rowland," has a remarkable resemblance to the dwellings of the " good folk," which recent excavations have revealed. By the kindness of Mr. MacRitchie, I am enabled to give the reader illustrations of one of the most interesting of these, the Maes-How of Orkney. This is a green mound some 100 feet in length and 35 in breadth at its broadest part. Tradition had long located a goblin in its centre, but it was not till 1861 that it was discovered to be pierced by a long passage 53 feet in length, and only two feet four inches high, for half of its length. This led into a central chamber

CENTRAL CHAMBER, MAES-HOW.

15 feet square and open to the sky. The diagrams on the opposite page will give all further details.

Now it is remarkable how accurately all this corresponds to the Dark Tower of " Childe Rowland," allowing for a little idealisation on

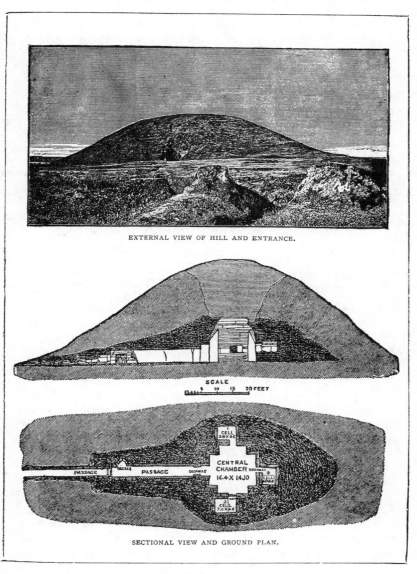

EXTERNAL VIEW OF HILL AND ENTRANCE.

SCALE

5   10   15   20 FEET

CELL
1
3.9 X 6.C

CENTRAL
CHAMBER
15.4 X 14.10

CELL
2

CELL
3
7.0 X 4.6

PASSAGE

RECESS

PASSAGE

DOORWAY

DOORWAY

SECTIONAL VIEW AND GROUND PLAN.

THE MAES HOW, ORKNEY.

the part of the narrator. We have the long dark passage leading into the well-lit central chamber, and all enclosed in a green hill or mound. It is of course curious to contrast Mr. Batten's frontispiece with the central chamber of the How, but the essential features are the same.

Even such a minute touch as the terraces on the hill have their bearing, I believe, on Mr. MacRitchie's "realistic" views of Faerie. For in quite another connection Mr. G. L. Gomme, in his book "The Village Community" (W. Scott), pp. 75–98, has given reasons

TERRACES AT NEWLANDS KIRK, PEEBLESHIRE.

and examples* for believing that terrace cultivation along the sides of hills was a practice of the non-Aryan and pre-Aryan inhabitants of these isles. Here then, from a quarter quite unexpected by Mr. MacRitchie, we have evidence of the association of the King of Elfland with a non-Aryan mode of cultivation of the soil. By Mr. Gomme's kindness I am enabled to give an illustration of this.

Altogether it seems not improbable that in such a tale as "Childe Rowland" we have an idealised picture of a "marriage by capture" of one of the diminutive non-Aryan dwellers of the green hills with an Aryan maiden, and her re-capture by her brothers. It is otherwise difficult to account for such a circumstantial description of the interior of these mounds, and especially of such a detail as the terrace cultivation on them. At the same time it must not be thought that Mr. MacRitchie's views explain all fairy tales, or that his identifications of Finns = Fenians = Fairies = Sidhe = "Pechs" = Picts, will necessarily be accepted. His interesting book, so far as it goes, seems to throw light on tales about mermaids (Finnish women in their "kayaks,") and trolls, but not necessarily on fairy tales in general. Thus, in the

---

* To these may be added Iona (*cf.* Duke of Argyll, *Iona*, p. 109).

present volume, besides "Childe Rowland," there is only "Tom Tit Tot" in his hollow, the green hill in "Kate Crackernuts," the "Cauld Lad of Hilton," and perhaps the "Fairy Ointment," that are affected by his views.

Though *Childe Rowland* may contain traces of primitive custom it is clear that in its present state it is of tolerably late date. We can, indeed, separate in it successive strata of social conditions. The extreme unction is Roman Catholic and yet the latest indication of the story, which must therefore date before 1530. The reference to the Childe, if meant to indicate the heir, is feudal in character, while the heirship of the younger son carries us back to "Borough English" and Anglo-Saxon times. The good brand that never struck in vain is at least of the Iron Age, while the Dark Tower, the terraces on the hills, and the Elfin King recall neolithic man with his cannibalism implied in the "Fee-fi-fo-fum." The story thus carries us through all the stages of civilisation up to the verge of modern times.

Finally, there are a couple of words in the narrative that deserve a couple of words of explanation : "Widershins" is probably, as Mr. Batten suggests, analogous to the German "wider Schein," against the appearance of the sun, "counterclockwise" as the mathematicians say—*i.e.*, W., S., E., N., instead of with the sun and the hands of a clock ; Mr. Gollancz in the *Academy* suggests "Wider Sinn," *i.e.*, in an opposite direction. "Bogle" is a provincial word for "spectre," and is analogous to the Welsh *bwg*, "goblin," and to the English insect of similar name, and still more curiously to the Russian "Bog," God, after which so many Russian rivers are named. I may add that "Burd" is etymologically the same as "bride," and is frequently used in the early romances for "Lady."

XXII. MOLLY WHUPPIE.

Source.—*Folk-Lore Journal*, ii. p. 68, forwarded by Rev. Walter Gregor. I have modified the dialect and changed "Mally" into "Molly."

Parallels.—The first part is clearly the theme of "Hop o' my Thumb," which Mr. Lang has studied in his "Perrault," pp. civ.-cxi. (*cf.* Köhler, *Occident*, ii. 301.) The change of night-dresses occurs in Greek myths. The latter part wanders off into "rob giant of three things," a familiar incident in folk-tales (Cosquin, i. 46-7), and finally winds up with the "out of sack" trick, for which see Cosquin, i. 113 ;

ii. 209 ; and Köhler, in *Occident und Orient*, ii. 489–506, on Campbell, No. xvii., Maol Chlioban, which was undoubtedly the source of our story. Kennedy's *Fireside Stories*, No. 1, "Hairy Rouchy" is exactly similar, showing the story to be originally Celtic.

XXIII. RED ETTIN.

Source.—"The Red Etin," in Chambers's *Pop. Rhymes of Scotland*, p. 89. I have reduced the adventures from three to two, and cut down the herds and their answers. I have substituted riddles from the first English collection of riddles, *The Demandes Joyous* of Wynkyn de Worde, for the poor ones of the original, which are besides not solved. "Ettin" is the English spelling of the word, as it is thus spelt in a passage of Beaumont and Fletcher (*Knight of Burning Pestle*, i. 1), which may refer to this very story, which, as we shall see, is quite as old as their time. It is the "Jötunn" of the Eddas (Dasent, *Norse Tales*, p. cxxvii.).

Parallels.—"The Red Etin" is referred to in *The Complaynt of Scotland*, about 1548. It has some resemblance to "Childe Rowland," which see. The "death index," as we may call tokens that tell the state of health of a parted partner, is a usual incident in the theme of the Two Brothers, and has been studied by the Grimms, i. 421, 453 ; ii. 403 ; by Köhler on Campbell, *Occ. u. Or.* ii. 119–20; on Gonzenbach, ii. 230; on Bladé, 248 ; by Cosquin, *l.c.*, i. 70-2, 193 ; by Crane, *Ital. Pop. Tales*, 326 ; and by Jones and Kropf, *Magyar Tales*, 329. Mr. Hartland devotes vol. ii. of his *Perseus* to the "Life Token." Riddles generally come in the form of the "riddle-bride-wager." (*cf.* Child, *Ballads*, i. 415–9 ; ii. 519), when the hero or heroine wins a spouse by guessing a riddle or riddles. Here it is the simpler Sphynx form of the "riddle task," on which see Köhler in *Jahrb. rom. Phil.*, vii. 273, and on Gonzenbach, 215.

XXIV. GOLDEN ARM.

Source.—Henderson, *l.c.*, p. 338, collected by the Rev. S. Baring-Gould, in Devonshire. Sir E. Burne-Jones remembers hearing it in his youth in Warwickshire, where I have also traces of it as "The Golden Leg."

Parallels.—The first fragment at the end of Grimm (ii. 467, of Mrs. Hunt's translation) tells of an innkeeper's wife who had used the liver of a man hanging on the gallows, whose ghost comes to her and tells her what has become of his hair, and his eyes, and the dialogue concludes

> " SHE : Where is thy liver?
> IT : Thou hast devoured it ! "

For similar "surprise packets' see Cosquin, ii. 77.

Remarks.—It is doubtful how far such gruesome topics should be introduced into a book for children, but, as a matter of fact, the κάθαρσις of pity and terror among the little ones is as effective as among the spectators of a drama, and they take the same kind of pleasant thrill from such stories. They know it is all make-believe just as much as the spectators of a tragedy. Every one who has enjoyed the blessing of a romantic imagination has been trained up on such tales of wonder.

XXV. TOM THUMB.

Source.—From the chap-book contained in Halliwell, p. 199, and Mr. Hartland's *English Folk and Fairy Tales*. I have omitted much of the second part.

Parallels.—Halliwell has also a version entirely in verse. "Tom Thumb" is "Le petit Poucet" of the French, "Daumling" of the Germans, and similar diminutive heroes elsewhere (*cf.* Deulin, *Contes de ma Mère l'Oye*, 326), but of his adventures only that in the cow's stomach (*cf.* Cosquin, ii. 190) is common with his French and German cousins. M. Gaston Paris has a monograph on "Tom Thumb."

XXVI. MR. FOX.

Source.—Contributed by Blakeway to Malone's Variorum Shakespeare, (1790) to illustrate Benedick's remark in *Much Ado about Nothing* (I. i. 146): "Like the old tale, my Lord, ' It is not so, nor 'twas not so, but, indeed, God forbid it should be so'"; which clearly refers to the tale of Mr. Fox. "The Forbidden Chamber" has been studied by Mr. Hartland, *Folk-Lore Journal*, iii. 193, *seq.* "Be bold" is Britomart's motto in the *Fairy Queen*, and one may also refer to "Bloody Jack" (*Ingoldsby*).

Parallels.—Halliwell, p. 166, gives a similar tale of "An Oxford Student," whose sweetheart saw him digging her grave. "Mr. Fox" is clearly a variant of the theme of "The Robber Bridegroom" (Grimm, No. 40, Mrs. Hunt's translation, i. 389, 395 ; and Cosquin, i. 180–1).

XXVII. LAZY JACK.

Source.—Halliwell, 157, from Yorkshire.

Parallels.—The same story occurs in Lowland Scotch as "Jock and his Mother," Chambers, *l.c.*, 101 ; in Ireland, as " I'll be wiser next time," Kennedy, *l.c.*, 39-42, and his *Fireside Stories*, p. 30. Abroad it is Grimm's *Hans im Gluck* (No. 83). The "cure by laughing" incident is "common form" in folk-tales (*cf.* Köhler on Gonzenbach, *Sizil. Märchen*, ii. 210, 224 ; Jones and Kropf, *Magyar Tales*, 312).

XXVIII. JOHNNY-CAKE.

Source.—*American Journal of Folk-Lore*, ii. 60 (*cf.* No. for July, 1991).

Parallels.—Another variant is given in the same *Journal*, p. 277, where reference is also made to a version, "The Gingerbread Boy," in *St. Nicholas*, May 1875. Chambers gives two versions of the same story, under the title "The Wee Bunnock," the first of which is one of the most dramatic and humorous of folk-tales. Unfortunately, the Scotticisms are so frequent as to render the Droll practically untranslatable. I have, however, made an attempt in *More English Fairy Tales*, lvii. Also in Ireland as "The Wonderful Cake" (Kennedy, *Fireside Stories*, p. 19.) "The Fate of Mr. Jack Sparrow" in *Uncle Remus* is similar to that of Johnny Cake.

XXIX. EARL MAR'S DAUGHTER.

Source.—From the ballad of the same name as given in Mr. Allingham's *Ballad Book :* it is clearly a fairy tale and not a ballad proper. The name Florentine is sufficient to prove that the tale does not belong to the Celtic area.

Parallels.—The lover visiting his spouse in guise of a bird is a frequent *motif* in folk-tales. The oldest known post-classic form occurs in Ireland in a prologue to the saga entitled "Togail Brudne da Derga," "The Destruction of da Derga's Fort," which must be as old as the early eleventh century, and is probably centuries older (*cf.* Mr. Nutt, *Folklore*, ii. 87).

XXX. MR. MIACCA.

Source.—From memory of Mrs. B. Abrahams, who heard it from her mother some *x* years ago (*x* > 40). I have transposed the two incidents, as in her version Tommy Grimes was a clever carver and carried about with him a carven leg. This seemed to me to exceed the limits of *vraisemblance* even for a folk-tale.

Parallels.—Getting out of an ogre's clutches by playing on the simplicity of his wife, occurs in " Molly Whuppie " (No. xxii.), and its similars. In the Grimms' " Hansel and Grethel," Hansel pokes out a stick instead of his finger that the witch may not think him fat enough for the table.

Remarks.—Mr. Miacca seems to have played the double *rôle* of a domestic Providence. He not alone punished bad boys, as here, but also rewarded the good, by leaving them gifts on appropriate occasions, like Santa Claus or Father Christmas, who, as is well known, only leaves things for good children. Mrs. Abrahams remembers one occasion well when she nearly caught sight of Mr. Miacca, just after he had left her a gift ; she saw his shadow in the shape of a bright light passing down the garden.

XXXI. DICK WHITTINGTON.

Source.—I have cobbled this up out of three chap-book versions : (1) that contained in Mr. Hartland's *English Folk-Tales ;* (2) that edited by Mr. H. B. Wheatley for the Villon Society ; (3) that appended to Messrs. Besant and Rice's monograph.

Parallels.—Whittington's cat has made the fortune of his master in all parts of the Old World, as Mr. W. A. Clouston, among others, has shown, *Popular Tales and Fictions*, ii. 65–78 (*cf.* Köhler on Gonzenbach, ii. 251).

Remarks.—If Bow Bells had pealed in the exact and accurate nineteenth century, they doubtless would have chimed

> Turn again, Whittington,
> Thrice and a half Lord Mayor of London.

For besides his three mayoralties of 1397, 1406, and 1419, he served as Lord Mayor in place of Adam Bamme, deceased, in the latter half of the mayoralty of 1396. It will be noticed that the chap-book puts the introduction of potatoes rather far back.

XXXII. THE STRANGE VISITOR.

Source.—From Chambers, *l.c.* 64, much Anglicised. I have retained "Aih-late wee moul," though I candidly confess I have not the slightest idea what it means ; judging other children by myself, I do not think that makes the response less effective. The prosaic-minded may substitute " Up-late-and-little food."

Parallels.—The man made by instalments, occurs in the Grimms, No. 4, and something like it in an English folk-tale, *The Golden Ball*, *ap.* Henderson, *l.c.*, p. 333 ; *cf.* "The Sprightly Tailor" in my *Celtic Fairy Tales.*

XXXIII. THE LAIDLY WORM.

Source.—From an eighteenth-century ballad of the Rev. Mr. Lamb of Norham, as given in Prof. Child's *Ballads ;* with a few touches and verses from the more ancient version "Kempion." A florid prose version appeared in *Monthly Chronicle of North Country Lore* for May 1890. I have made the obvious emendation of

" O quit your sword, unbend your bow."

for

" O quit your sword, and bend your bow."

The story is still extant near Bamborough, Mrs. Balfour informs me.

Parallels.—The ballad of "Kempe Owein" is a more general version which "The Laidly Worm" has localised near Bamborough. We learn from this that the original herd was Kempe or Champion Owain, the Welsh hero who flourished in the sixth century. Childe Wynd therefore = Childe Owein. The "Deliverance Kiss" has been studied by Prof. Child, *l.c..*, ii. 306. A noteworthy example occurs in Boiardo's *Orlando Inamorato*, cc. xxv., xxvi.

Remarks.—It is perhaps unnecessary to give the equations " Laidly Worm = Loathly Worm = Loathsome Dragon," and " borrowed = changed." On the rowan tree, see Rhys' *Hibbert Lectures.* There is certainly something Celtic about the Laidly being and the deliverance kiss, as Mr. Nutt has pointed out, *Academy*, April 30, 1892, and Miss Weston has shown the connection in her *Legend of Sir Gawain*, p. 49. Indeed, may not Owein be identical with Gawain ?

XXXIV. CAT AND MOUSE.

Source.—Halliwell, p. 154.

Parallels.—Scarcely more than a variant of the " Old Woman and her Pig" (No. iv.), which see. It is curious that a very similar " run " is added by Bengali women at the end of every folk-tale they tell (Lal Behari Day, *Folk Tales of Bengal*, Pref. *ad fin.*)

XXXV. THE FISH AND THE RING.

Source.—Henderson, *l.c.*, p. 326, from a communication by the Rev. S. Baring-Gould. There is a similar legend told of Stepney Church.

Parallels.—" Jonah rings " have been put together by Mr. Clouston in his *Popular Tales*, i. 398, &c. : the most famous are those of Poly-crates, of Solomon, and the Sanskrit drama of " Sakuntala," the plot of which turns upon such a ring. " Letters to kill bearer " have been traced from Homer downwards by Prof. Köhler on Gonzenbach, ii. 220, and " the substituted letter " by the same authority in *Occ. u. Or.*, ii. 289. Mr. Baring-Gould, who was one of the pioneers of the study of folk-tales in this country, has given a large number of in-stances of " the preordained marriage " in folk-tales in Henderson, *l.c.*

Remarks.—The tale is the feminine form of the legend of " The Man born to be King," familiar to us from Mr. Morris's setting in his *Earthly Paradise.* He derived this from *Nouvelles Françoises du Treizième Siècle*, which he has himself translated under the title *Old French Romances.* In my introduction to his translation I have pointed out that this particular romance has a Byzantine source, an Ethiopic version of which has recently been discovered by Dr. E. Kuhn. The story is, indeed, told under the title of *Coustant the Emperor* as a sort of folk etymology of the name Constantinople. It seems probable that the tale was thus brought from Byzantium to France and England and became localised in different forms at Stepney and York. Curiously enough, the letter to "kill bearer" is found in India, and is of course familiar from the *Iliad*. But, what-ever its ultimate source, there can be little doubt that this tale is more immediately derived from the Byzantine Romance of the Emperor Constant.

XXXVI. THE MAGPIE'S NEST.

Source.—I have built up the " Magpie's Nest " from two nidifica-
tion myths, as a German professor would call them, in the Rev.
Mr. Swainson's *Folk-Lore of British Birds*, pp. 80 and 166. I have received instruction about the relative values of nests from a little
friend of mine named Katie, who knows all about it. If there is
any mistake in the order of neatness in the various birds' nests, I
must have learnt my lesson badly.

Remarks.—English popular tradition is curiously at variance about
the magpie's nidificatory powers, for another legend given by Mr.
Swainson represents her as refusing to be instructed by the birds,
and that is why she does *not* make a good nest. The latter part of
our tale occurs in the Welsh " Fables of Catwg " in the *Iolo MS.*

XXXVII. KATE CRACKERNUTS.

Source.—Given by Mr. Lang in *Longmans' Magazine*, vol. xiv., and
reprinted in *Folk-Lore*, Sept. 1890. It is very corrupt, both girls being
called Kate, and I have had largely to rewrite.

Parallels.—There is a tale which is clearly a cousin if not a parent
of this in Kennedy's *Fictions*, 54 *seq.*, containing the visit to the green
hill (for which see "Childe Rowland"), a reference to nuts, and even
the sesame rhyme. The Prince is here a corpse who becomes revivi-
fied ; the same story is in Campbell, No. 13. The jealous stepmother
is " universally human." (*Cf.* Köhler on Gonzenbach, ii. 206.) Though
I have suggested in *Indian Fairy Tales* that she was originally a
jealous co-wife.

XXXVIII. THE CAULD LAD OF HILTON.

Source.—Henderson's *Folk-lore of Northern Counties*, 2nd edition,
published by the Folk-lore Society, pp. 266–7. I have written the
introductory paragraph so as to convey some information about
Brownies, Bogles, and Redcaps, for which Henderson, *l.c.*, 246–53, is
my authority. Mr. Batten's portrait renders this somewhat superfluous.

Parallels.—The Grimms' " Elves " (No. 39) behave in like manner
on being rewarded for their services. Milton's "lubbar-fiend" in
L'Allegro has all the characteristics of a Brownie.

XXXIX. ASS, TABLE, AND STICK.

Source.—Henderson, *l.c.*, first edition, pp. 327-9, by the Rev. S. Baring-Gould.

Parallels.—Mr. Baring-Gould gives another version from the East Riding, *l.c.*, 329, in which there are three brothers who go through the adventures. He also refers to European Variants, p. 311, which could now be largely supplemented from Cosquin, i. 53-4, ii. 66, 171. To these add the Irish versions of Kennedy, *Fireside Stories*, p. 25, "The Three Gifts," and Croker *Fairy Legends*, "The Legend of Bottle Hill."

Remarks.—As an example of the sun-myth explanation of folk-tales I will quote the same authority (p. 314) : "The Master, who gives the three precious gifts, is the All Father, the Supreme Spirit. The gold and jewel-dropping ass, is the spring cloud, hanging in the sky and shedding the bright productive vernal showers. The table which covers itself is the earth becoming covered with flowers and fruit at the bidding of the new year. But there is a check ; rain is withheld, the process of vegetation is stayed by some evil influence. Then comes the thunder cloud, out of which leaps the bolt ; the rains pour down, the earth receives them, and is covered with abundance—all that was lost is recovered."

XL. FAIRY OINTMENT.

Source.—Mrs. Bray, *The Tamar and the Tavy*, i. 74 (letters to Southey), as quoted by Mr. Hartland in *Folk-Lore*, i. 207-8. I have christened the anonymous midwife and euphemised her profession.

Parallels.—Mr. Hartland has studied Human Midwives in the *Archæol. Review*, iv., and parallels to our story in *Folk-Lore*, i. 209, *seq.*; the most interesting of these is from Gervase of Tilbury (xiii. cent.), *Otia Imper.*, iii. 85, and three Breton tales given by M. Sébillot (*Contes*, ii. 42 ; *Litt. orale*, 23 ; *Trad. et Superst.*, i. 109). *Cf.* Prof. Child, i. 339 ; ii. 505. A Welsh one is given in *Y Cymmrodor*, vii. 197. Mr. Hartland has summarised his conclusions in his *Science of Fairy Tales*.

XLI. THE WELL OF THE WORLD'S END.

Source.—Leyden's edition of *The Complaynt of Scotland*, p. 234, *seq.*, with additional touches from Halliwell, 162–3, who makes up a slightly different version from the rhymes. The opening formula I have taken from Mayhew, *London Labour*, iii. 390, who gives it as the usual one when tramps tell folk-tales. I also added it to No. xvii.

Parallels.—Sir W. Scott remembered a similar story; see Taylor's *Gammer Grethel, ad fin.* In Scotland it is Chambers's tale of *The Paddo*, p. 87; Leyden supposes it is referred to in the *Complaynt* (c. 1548), as "The Wolf of the Worldis End." The well of this name occurs also in the Scotch version of the "Three Heads of the Well" (No. xliii.). Abroad it is the Grimms' first tale, while frogs who would a-wooing go are discussed by Prof. Köhler, *Occ. u. Orient.*, ii. 330 ; by Prof. Child, i. 298 ; and by Messrs. Jones and Kropf, *l.c.*, p. 404. The sieve-bucket task is widespread from the Danaids of the Greeks to the leverets of *Uncle Remus*, who, curiously enough, use the same rhyme : " Fill it wid moss en dob it wid clay." *Cf.*, too, No. xxiii.

XLII. MASTER OF ALL MASTERS.

Source.—I have taken what suited me from a number of sources which shows how widespread this quaint droll is in England : (i) In Mayhew, *London Poor*, iii. 391, told by a lad in a workhouse ; (ii) several versions in 7 *Notes and Queries*, iii. 35, 87, 159, 398.

Parallels.—Rev. W. Gregor gives a Scotch version under the title " The Clever Apprentice," in *Folk-Lore Journal*, vii. 166. An Irish version with the Gaelic was given in *Folk-Lore* for March 1891. Mr. Hartland, in *Notes and Queries*, *l.c.*, 87, refers to Pitré's *Fiabi sicil.*, iii. 120, for a variant.

Remarks.—According to Mr. Hartland, the story is designed as a satire on pedantry, and is as old in Italy as Straparola (sixteenth century). In passionate Sicily a wife disgusted with her husband's pedantry sets the house on fire, and informs her husband of the fact in his own unintelligible gibberish; he, not understanding his own lingo, falls a victim to the flames, and she marries the servant who had taken the message.

XLIII. THE THREE HEADS OF THE WELL.

Source.—Halliwell, p. 158, from a chap-book. The second wish has been somewhat euphemised.

Parallels.—The story forms part of Peele's *Old Wives' Tale*, where the rhyme was

> "*A Head rises in the well,*
> Fair maiden, white and red,
> Stroke me smooth and comb my head,
> And thou shalt have some cockell-bread."

It is also in Chambers, *l.c.*, 105, where the well is at the World's End (*cf.* No. xli.). The contrasted fates of two step-sisters, is the Frau Holle (Grimm, No. 24) type of Folk-tale studied by Cosquin, i. 250, *seq.* "Kate Crackernuts" (No. xxxvii.) is a pleasant contrast to this.

A CATALOG OF SELECTED DOVER BOOKS IN ALL FIELDS OF INTEREST

CONCERNING THE SPIRITUAL IN ART, Wassily Kandinsky. Pioneering work by father of abstract art. Thoughts on color theory, nature of art. Analysis of earlier masters. 12 illustrations. 80pp. of text. 5⅜ × 8½. 23411-8 Pa. $2.95

LEONARDO ON THE HUMAN BODY, Leonardo da Vinci. More than 1200 of Leonardo's anatomical drawings on 215 plates. Leonardo's text, which accompanies the drawings, has been translated into English. 506pp. 8⅜ × 11¾. 24483-0 Pa. $11.95

GOBLIN MARKET, Christina Rossetti. Best-known work by poet comparable to Emily Dickinson, Alfred Tennyson. With 46 delightfully grotesque illustrations by Laurence Housman. 64pp. 4 × 6¾. 24516-0 Pa. $2.50

THE HEART OF THOREAU'S JOURNALS, edited by Odell Shepard. Selections from *Journal*, ranging over full gamut of interests. 228pp. 5⅜ × 8½. 20741-2 Pa. $4.50

MR. LINCOLN'S CAMERA MAN: MATHEW B. BRADY, Roy Meredith. Over 300 Brady photos reproduced directly from original negatives, photos. Lively commentary. 368pp. 8⅜ × 11¼. 23021-X Pa. $14.95

PHOTOGRAPHIC VIEWS OF SHERMAN'S CAMPAIGN, George N. Barnard. Reprint of landmark 1866 volume with 61 plates: battlefield of New Hope Church, the Etawah Bridge, the capture of Atlanta, etc. 80pp. 9 × 12. 23445-2 Pa. $6.00

A SHORT HISTORY OF ANATOMY AND PHYSIOLOGY FROM THE GREEKS TO HARVEY, Dr. Charles Singer. Thoroughly engrossing non-technical survey. 270 illustrations. 211pp. 5⅜ × 8½. 20389-1 Pa. $4.95

REDOUTE ROSES IRON-ON TRANSFER PATTERNS, Barbara Christopher. Redouté was botanical painter to the Empress Josephine; transfer his famous roses onto fabric with these 24 transfer patterns. 80pp. 8¼ × 10⅞. 24292-7 Pa. $3.50

THE FIVE BOOKS OF ARCHITECTURE, Sebastiano Serlio. Architectural milestone, first (1611) English translation of Renaissance classic. Unabridged reproduction of original edition includes over 300 woodcut illustrations. 416pp. 9⅝ × 12¼. 24349-4 Pa. $14.95

CARLSON'S GUIDE TO LANDSCAPE PAINTING, John F. Carlson. Authoritative, comprehensive guide covers, every aspect of landscape painting. 34 reproductions of paintings by author; 58 explanatory diagrams. 144pp. 8⅜ × 11. 22927-0 Pa. $5.95

101 PUZZLES IN THOUGHT AND LOGIC, C.R. Wylie, Jr. Solve murders, robberies, see which fishermen are liars—purely by reasoning! 107pp. 5⅜ × 8½. 20367-0 Pa. $2.00

TEST YOUR LOGIC, George J. Summers. 50 more truly new puzzles with new turns of thought, new subtleties of inference. 100pp. 5⅜ × 8½. 22877-0 Pa. $2.50

THE MURDER BOOK OF J.G. REEDER, Edgar Wallace. Eight suspenseful stories by bestselling mystery writer of 20s and 30s. Features the donnish Mr. J.G. Reeder of Public Prosecutor's Office. 128pp. 5⅜ × 8½.
24374-5 Pa. $3.95

ANNE ORR'S CHARTED DESIGNS, Anne Orr. Best designs by premier needlework designer, all on charts: flowers, borders, birds, children, alphabets, etc. Over 100 charts, 10 in color. Total of 40pp. 8¼ × 11. 23704-4 Pa. $2.50

BASIC CONSTRUCTION TECHNIQUES FOR HOUSES AND SMALL BUILDINGS SIMPLY EXPLAINED, U.S. Bureau of Naval Personnel. Grading, masonry, woodworking, floor and wall framing, roof framing, plastering, tile setting, much more. Over 675 illustrations. 568pp. 6½ × 9¼. 20242-9 Pa. $9.95

MATISSE LINE DRAWINGS AND PRINTS, Henri Matisse. Representative collection of female nudes, faces, still lifes, experimental works, etc., from 1898 to 1948. 50 illustrations. 48pp. 8⅜ × 11¼. 23877-6 Pa. $3.50

HOW TO PLAY THE CHESS OPENINGS, Eugene Znosko-Borovsky. Clear, profound examinations of just what each opening is intended to do and how opponent can counter. Many sample games. 147pp. 5⅜ × 8½. 22795-2 Pa. $3.50

DUPLICATE BRIDGE, Alfred Sheinwold. Clear, thorough, easily followed account: rules, etiquette, scoring, strategy, bidding; Goren's point-count system, Blackwood and Gerber conventions, etc. 158pp. 5⅜ × 8½. 22741-3 Pa. $3.50

SARGENT PORTRAIT DRAWINGS, J.S. Sargent. Collection of 42 portraits reveals technical skill and intuitive eye of noted American portrait painter, John Singer Sargent. 48pp. 8¼ × 11⅛. 24524-1 Pa. $3.50

ENTERTAINING SCIENCE EXPERIMENTS WITH EVERYDAY OBJECTS, Martin Gardner. Over 100 experiments for youngsters. Will amuse, astonish, teach, and entertain. Over 100 illustrations. 127pp. 5⅜ × 8½. 24201-3 Pa. $2.50

TEDDY BEAR PAPER DOLLS IN FULL COLOR: A Family of Four Bears and Their Costumes, Crystal Collins. A family of four Teddy Bear paper dolls and nearly 60 cut-out costumes. Full color, printed one side only. 32pp. 9¼ × 12¼.
24550-0 Pa. $3.50

NEW CALLIGRAPHIC ORNAMENTS AND FLOURISHES, Arthur Baker. Unusual, multi-useable material: arrows, pointing hands, brackets and frames, ovals, swirls, birds, etc. Nearly 700 illustrations. 80pp. 8⅜ × 11¼.
24095-9 Pa. $3.75

DINOSAUR DIORAMAS TO CUT & ASSEMBLE, M. Kalmenoff. Two complete three-dimensional scenes in full color, with 31 cut-out animals and plants. Excellent educational toy for youngsters. Instructions; 2 assembly diagrams. 32pp. 9¼ × 12¼. 24541-1 Pa. $4.50

SILHOUETTES: A PICTORIAL ARCHIVE OF VARIED ILLUSTRATIONS, edited by Carol Belanger Grafton. Over 600 silhouettes from the 18th to 20th centuries. Profiles and full figures of men, women, children, birds, animals, groups and scenes, nature, ships, an alphabet. 144pp. 8⅜ × 11¼. 23781-8 Pa. $5.95

25 KITES THAT FLY, Leslie Hunt. Full, easy-to-follow instructions for kites made from inexpensive materials. Many novelties. 70 illustrations. 110pp. 5⅜ × 8½.
22550-X Pa. $2.50

PIANO TUNING, J. Cree Fischer. Clearest, best book for beginner, amateur. Simple repairs, raising dropped notes, tuning by easy method of flattened fifths. No previous skills needed. 4 illustrations. 201pp. 5⅜ × 8½. 23267-0 Pa. $3.50

EARLY AMERICAN IRON-ON TRANSFER PATTERNS, edited by Rita Weiss. 75 designs, borders, alphabets, from traditional American sources. 48pp. 8¼ × 11.
23162-3 Pa. $1.95

CROCHETING EDGINGS, edited by Rita Weiss. Over 100 of the best designs for these lovely trims for a host of household items. Complete instructions, illustrations. 48pp. 8¼ × 11. 24031-2 Pa. $2.95

FINGER PLAYS FOR NURSERY AND KINDERGARTEN, Emilie Poulsson. 18 finger plays with music (voice and piano); entertaining, instructive. Counting, nature lore, etc. Victorian classic. 53 illustrations. 80pp. 6½ × 9¼. 22588-7 Pa. $2.25

BOSTON THEN AND NOW, Peter Vanderwarker. Here in 59 side-by-side views are photographic documentations of the city's past and present. 119 photographs. Full captions. 122pp. 8¼ × 11. 24312-5 Pa. $7.95

CROCHETING BEDSPREADS, edited by Rita Weiss. 22 patterns, originally published in three instruction books 1939-41. 39 photos, 8 charts. Instructions. 48pp. 8¼ × 11. 23610-2 Pa. $2.00

HAWTHORNE ON PAINTING, Charles W. Hawthorne. Collected from notes taken by students at famous Cape Cod School; hundreds of direct, personal *apercus*, ideas, suggestions. 91pp. 5⅜ × 8½. 20653-X Pa. $2.95

THERMODYNAMICS, Enrico Fermi. A classic of modern science. Clear, organized treatment of systems, first and second laws, entropy, thermodynamic potentials, etc. Calculus required. 160pp. 5⅜ × 8½. 60361-X Pa. $4.50

TEN BOOKS ON ARCHITECTURE, Vitruvius. The most important book ever written on architecture. Early Roman aesthetics, technology, classical orders, site selection, all other aspects. Morgan translation. 331pp. 5⅜ × 8½. 20645-9 Pa. $6.95

THE CORNELL BREAD BOOK, Clive M. McCay and Jeanette B. McCay. Famed high-protein recipe incorporated into breads, rolls, buns, coffee cakes, pizza, pie crusts, more. Nearly 50 illustrations. 48pp. 8¼ × 11. 23995-0 Pa. $2.00

THE CRAFTSMAN'S HANDBOOK, Cennino Cennini. 15th-century handbook, school of Giotto, explains applying gold, silver leaf; gesso; fresco painting, grinding pigments, etc. 142pp. 6⅛ × 9¼. 20054-X Pa. $3.95

FRANK LLOYD WRIGHT'S FALLINGWATER, Donald Hoffmann. Full story of Wright's masterwork at Bear Run, Pa. 100 photographs of site, construction, and details of completed structure. 112pp. 9¼ × 10. 23671-4 Pa. $7.95

OVAL STAINED GLASS PATTERN BOOK, C. Eaton. 60 new designs framed in shape of an oval. Greater complexity, challenge with sinuous cats, birds, mandalas framed in antique shape. 64pp. 8¼ × 11. 24519-5 Pa. $3.95

THE BOOK OF WOOD CARVING, Charles Marshall Sayers. Still finest book for beginning student. Fundamentals, technique; gives 34 designs, over 34 projects for panels, bookends, mirrors, etc. 33 photos. 118pp. 7¾ × 10⅝. 23654-4 Pa. $3.95

CARVING COUNTRY CHARACTERS, Bill Higginbotham. Expert advice for beginning, advanced carvers on materials, techniques for creating 18 projects— mirthful panorama of American characters. 105 illustrations. 80pp. 8⅜ × 11. 24135-1 Pa. $2.95

300 ART NOUVEAU DESIGNS AND MOTIFS IN FULL COLOR, C.B. Grafton. 44 full-page plates display swirling lines and muted colors typical of Art Nouveau. Borders, frames, panels, cartouches, dingbats, etc. 48pp. 9⅜ × 12¼. 24354-0 Pa. $6.95

SELF-WORKING CARD TRICKS, Karl Fulves. Editor of *Pallbearer* offers 72 tricks that work automatically through nature of card deck. No sleight of hand needed. Often spectacular. 42 illustrations. 113pp. 5⅜ × 8½. 23334-0 Pa. $3.50

CUT AND ASSEMBLE A WESTERN FRONTIER TOWN, Edmund V. Gillon, Jr. Ten authentic full-color buildings on heavy cardboard stock in H-O scale. Sheriff's Office and Jail, Saloon, Wells Fargo, Opera House, others. 48pp. 9¼ × 12¼. 23736-2 Pa. $4.95

CUT AND ASSEMBLE AN EARLY NEW ENGLAND VILLAGE, Edmund V. Gillon, Jr. Printed in full color on heavy cardboard stock. 12 authentic buildings in H-O scale: Adams home in Quincy, Mass., Oliver Wight house in Sturbridge, smithy, store, church, others. 48pp. 9¼ × 12¼. 23536-X Pa. $4.95

THE TALE OF TWO BAD MICE, Beatrix Potter. Tom Thumb and Hunca Munca squeeze out of their hole and go exploring. 27 full-color Potter illustrations. 59pp. 4¼ × 5½. (Available in U.S. only) 23065-1 Pa. $1.75

CARVING FIGURE CARICATURES IN THE OZARK STYLE, Harold L. Enlow. Instructions and illustrations for ten delightful projects, plus general carving instructions. 22 drawings and 47 photographs altogether. 39pp. 8⅜ × 11. 23151-8 Pa. $2.95

A TREASURY OF FLOWER DESIGNS FOR ARTISTS, EMBROIDERERS AND CRAFTSMEN, Susan Gaber. 100 garden favorites lushly rendered by artist for artists, craftsmen, needleworkers. Many form frames, borders. 80pp. 8¼ × 11. 24096-7 Pa. $3.95

CUT & ASSEMBLE A TOY THEATER/THE NUTCRACKER BALLET, Tom Tierney. Model of a complete, full-color production of Tchaikovsky's classic. 6 backdrops, dozens of characters, familiar dance sequences. 32pp. 9⅜ × 12¼. 24194-7 Pa. $4.50

ANIMALS: 1,419 COPYRIGHT-FREE ILLUSTRATIONS OF MAMMALS, BIRDS, FISH, INSECTS, ETC., edited by Jim Harter. Clear wood engravings present, in extremely lifelike poses, over 1,000 species of animals. 284pp. 9 × 12. 23766-4 Pa. $9.95

MORE HAND SHADOWS, Henry Bursill. For those at their 'finger ends,'' 16 more effects—Shakespeare, a hare, a squirrel, Mr. Punch, and twelve more—each explained by a full-page illustration. Considerable period charm. 30pp. 6½ × 9¼. 21384-6 Pa. $1.95

SURREAL STICKERS AND UNREAL STAMPS, William Rowe. 224 haunting, hilarious stamps on gummed, perforated stock, with images of elephants, geisha girls, George Washington, etc. 16pp. one side. 8¼ × 11.   24371-0 Pa. $3.50

GOURMET KITCHEN LABELS, Ed Sibbett, Jr. 112 full-color labels (4 copies each of 28 designs). Fruit, bread, other culinary motifs. Gummed and perforated. 16pp. 8¼ × 11.   24087-8 Pa. $2.95

PATTERNS AND INSTRUCTIONS FOR CARVING AUTHENTIC BIRDS, H.D. Green. Detailed instructions, 27 diagrams, 85 photographs for carving 15 species of birds so life-like, they'll seem ready to fly! 8¼ × 11.   24222-6 Pa. $3.00

FLATLAND, E.A. Abbott. Science-fiction classic explores life of 2-D being in 3-D world. 16 illustrations. 103pp. 5⅜ × 8.   20001-9 Pa. $2.00

DRIED FLOWERS, Sarah Whitlock and Martha Rankin. Concise, clear, practical guide to dehydration, glycerinizing, pressing plant material, and more. Covers use of silica gel. 12 drawings. 32pp. 5⅜ × 8½.   21802-3 Pa. $1.00

EASY-TO-MAKE CANDLES, Gary V. Guy. Learn how easy it is to make all kinds of decorative candles. Step-by-step instructions. 82 illustrations. 48pp. 8¼ × 11.
     23881-4 Pa. $2.95

SUPER STICKERS FOR KIDS, Carolyn Bracken. 128 gummed and perforated full-color stickers: GIRL WANTED, KEEP OUT, BORED OF EDUCATION, X-RATED, COMBAT ZONE, many others. 16pp. 8¼ × 11.   24092-4 Pa. $3.50

CUT AND COLOR PAPER MASKS, Michael Grater. Clowns, animals, funny faces...simply color them in, cut them out, and put them together, and you have 9 paper masks to play with and enjoy. 32pp. 8¼ × 11.   23171-2 Pa. $2.95

A CHRISTMAS CAROL: THE ORIGINAL MANUSCRIPT, Charles Dickens. Clear facsimile of Dickens manuscript, on facing pages with final printed text. 8 illustrations by John Leech, 4 in color on covers. 144pp. 8⅜ × 11¼.
     20980-6 Pa. $5.95

CARVING SHOREBIRDS, Harry V. Shourds & Anthony Hillman. 16 full-size patterns (all double-page spreads) for 19 North American shorebirds with step-by-step instructions. 72pp. 9¼ × 12¼.   24287-0 Pa. $5.95

THE GENTLE ART OF MATHEMATICS, Dan Pedoe. Mathematical games, probability, the question of infinity, topology, how the laws of algebra work, problems of irrational numbers, and more. 42 figures. 143pp. 5⅜ × 8½.
     22949-1 Pa. $3.50

READY-TO-USE DOLLHOUSE WALLPAPER, Katzenbach & Warren, Inc. Stripe, 2 floral stripes, 2 allover florals, polka dot; all in full color. 4 sheets (350 sq. in.) of each, enough for average room. 48pp. 8¼ × 11.   23495-9 Pa. $2.95

MINIATURE IRON-ON TRANSFER PATTERNS FOR DOLLHOUSES, DOLLS, AND SMALL PROJECTS, Rita Weiss and Frank Fontana. Over 100 miniature patterns: rugs, bedspreads, quilts, chair seats, etc. In standard dollhouse size. 48pp. 8¼ × 11.   23741-9 Pa. $1.95

THE DINOSAUR COLORING BOOK, Anthony Rao. 45 renderings of dinosaurs, fossil birds, turtles, other creatures of Mesozoic Era. Scientifically accurate. Captions. 48pp. 8¼ × 11.   24022-3 Pa. $2.50

JAPANESE DESIGN MOTIFS, Matsuya Co. Mon, or heraldic designs. Over 4000 typical, beautiful designs: birds, animals, flowers, swords, fans, geometrics; all beautifully stylized. 213pp. 11⅜ × 8¼. 22874-6 Pa. $7.95

THE TALE OF BENJAMIN BUNNY, Beatrix Potter. Peter Rabbit's cousin coaxes him back into Mr. McGregor's garden for a whole new set of adventures. All 27 full-color illustrations. 59pp. 4¼ × 5½. (Available in U.S. only) 21102-9 Pa. $1.75

THE TALE OF PETER RABBIT AND OTHER FAVORITE STORIES BOXED SET, Beatrix Potter. Seven of Beatrix Potter's best-loved tales including Peter Rabbit in a specially designed, durable boxed set. 4¼ × 5½. Total of 447pp. 158 color illustrations. (Available in U.S. only) 23903-9 Pa. $12.25

PRACTICAL MENTAL MAGIC, Theodore Annemann. Nearly 200 astonishing feats of mental magic revealed in step-by-step detail. Complete advice on staging, patter, etc. Illustrated. 320pp. 5⅜ × 8½. 24426-1 Pa. $5.95

CELEBRATED CASES OF JUDGE DEE (DEE GOONG AN), translated by Robert Van Gulik. Authentic 18th-century Chinese detective novel; Dee and associates solve three interlocked cases. Led to van Gulik's own stories with same characters. Extensive introduction. 9 illustrations. 237pp. 5⅜ × 8½. 23337-5 Pa. $4.95

CUT & FOLD EXTRATERRESTRIAL INVADERS THAT FLY, M. Grater. Stage your own lilliputian space battles.By following the step-by-step instructions and explanatory diagrams you can launch 22 full-color fliers into space. 36pp. 8¼ × 11. 24478-4 Pa. $2.95

CUT & ASSEMBLE VICTORIAN HOUSES, Edmund V. Gillon, Jr. Printed in full color on heavy cardboard stock, 4 authentic Victorian houses in H-O scale: Italian-style Villa, Octagon, Second Empire, Stick Style. 48pp. 9¼ × 12¼. 23849-0 Pa. $4.95

BEST SCIENCE FICTION STORIES OF H.G. WELLS, H.G. Wells. Full novel *The Invisible Man,* plus 17 short stories: "The Crystal Egg," "Aepyornis Island," "The Strange Orchid," etc. 303pp. 5⅜ × 8½. (Available in U.S. only) 21531-8 Pa. $4.95

TRADEMARK DESIGNS OF THE WORLD, Yusaku Kamekura. A lavish collection of nearly 700 trademarks, the work of Wright, Loewy, Klee, Binder, hundreds of others. 160pp. 8¾ × 8. (EJ) 24191-2 Pa. $5.95

THE ARTIST'S AND CRAFTSMAN'S GUIDE TO REDUCING, ENLARGING AND TRANSFERRING DESIGNS, Rita Weiss. Discover, reduce, enlarge, transfer designs from any objects to any craft project. 12pp. plus 16 sheets special graph paper. 8¼ × 11. 24142-4 Pa. $3.95

TREASURY OF JAPANESE DESIGNS AND MOTIFS FOR ARTISTS AND CRAFTSMEN, edited by Carol Belanger Grafton. Indispensable collection of 360 traditional Japanese designs and motifs redrawn in clean, crisp black-and-white, copyright-free illustrations. 96pp. 8¼ × 11. 24435-0 Pa. $4.50

CHANCERY CURSIVE STROKE BY STROKE, Arthur Baker. Instructions and illustrations for each stroke of each letter (upper and lower case) and numerals. 54 full-page plates. 64pp. 8¼ × 11. 24278-1 Pa. $2.50

THE ENJOYMENT AND USE OF COLOR, Walter Sargent. Color relationships, values, intensities; complementary colors, illumination, similar topics. Color in nature and art. 7 color plates, 29 illustrations. 274pp. 5⅜ × 8½. 20944-X Pa. $4.95

SCULPTURE PRINCIPLES AND PRACTICE, Louis Slobodkin. Step-by-step approach to clay, plaster, metals, stone; classical and modern. 253 drawings, photos. 255pp. 8⅛ × 11. 22960-2 Pa. $7.50

VICTORIAN FASHION PAPER DOLLS FROM HARPER'S BAZAR, 1867-1898, Theodore Menten. Four female dolls with 28 elegant high fashion costumes, printed in full color. 32pp. 9¼ × 12¼. 23453-3 Pa. $3.95

FLOPSY, MOPSY AND COTTONTAIL: A Little Book of Paper Dolls in Full Color, Susan LaBelle. Three dolls and 21 costumes (7 for each doll) show Peter Rabbit's siblings dressed for holidays, gardening, hiking, etc. Charming borders, captions. 48pp. 4¼ × 5½. (USCO) 24376-1 Pa. $2.50

NATIONAL LEAGUE BASEBALL CARD CLASSICS, Bert Randolph Sugar. 83 big-leaguers from 1909-69 on facsimile cards. Hubbell, Dean, Spahn, Brock plus advertising, info, no duplications. Perforated, detachable. 16pp. 8¼ × 11.
24308-7 Pa. $3.50

THE LOGICAL APPROACH TO CHESS, Dr. Max Euwe, et al. First-rate text of comprehensive strategy, tactics, theory for the amateur. No gambits to memorize, just a clear, logical approach. 224pp. 5⅜ × 8½. 24353-2 Pa. $4.50

MAGICK IN THEORY AND PRACTICE, Aleister Crowley. The summation of the thought and practice of the century's most famous necromancer, long hard to find. Crowley's best book. 436pp. 5⅜ × 8½. (Available in U.S. only)
23295-6 Pa. $6.95

THE HAUNTED HOTEL, Wilkie Collins. Collins' last great tale; doom and destiny in a Venetian palace. Praised by T.S. Eliot. 127pp. 5⅜ × 8½.
24333-8 Pa. $3.00

ART DECO DISPLAY ALPHABETS, Dan X. Solo. Wide variety of bold yet elegant lettering in handsome Art Deco styles. 100 complete fonts, with numerals, punctuation, more. 104pp. 8⅛ × 11. 24372-9 Pa. $4.50

CALLIGRAPHIC ALPHABETS, Arthur Baker. Nearly 150 complete alphabets by outstanding contemporary. Stimulating ideas; useful source for unique effects. 154 plates. 157pp. 8⅜ × 11¼. 21045-6 Pa. $5.95

ARTHUR BAKER'S HISTORIC CALLIGRAPHIC ALPHABETS, Arthur Baker. From monumental capitals of first-century Rome to humanistic cursive of 16th century, 33 alphabets in fresh interpretations. 88 plates. 96pp. 9 × 12.
24054-1 Pa. $4.50

LETTIE LANE PAPER DOLLS, Sheila Young. Genteel turn-of-the-century family very popular then and now. 24 paper dolls. 16 plates in full color. 32pp. 9¼ × 12¼. 24089-4 Pa. $3.95

KEYBOARD WORKS FOR SOLO INSTRUMENTS, G.F. Handel. 35 neglected works from Handel's vast oeuvre, originally jotted down as improvisations. Includes Eight Great Suites, others. New sequence. 174pp. 9⅜ × 12¼.
24338-9 Pa. $7.50

AMERICAN LEAGUE BASEBALL CARD CLASSICS, Bert Randolph Sugar. 82 stars from 1900s to 60s on facsimile cards. Ruth, Cobb, Mantle, Williams, plus advertising, info, no duplications. Perforated, detachable. 16pp. 8¼ × 11.
24286-2 Pa. $3.50

A TREASURY OF CHARTED DESIGNS FOR NEEDLEWORKERS, Georgia Gorham and Jeanne Warth. 141 charted designs: owl, cat with yarn, tulips, piano, spinning wheel, covered bridge, Victorian house and many others. 48pp. 8¼ × 11.
23558-0 Pa. $1.95

DANISH FLORAL CHARTED DESIGNS, Gerda Bengtsson. Exquisite collection of over 40 different florals: anemone, Iceland poppy, wild fruit, pansies, many others. 45 illustrations. 48pp. 8¼ × 11. 23957-8 Pa. $2.50

OLD PHILADELPHIA IN EARLY PHOTOGRAPHS 1839-1914, Robert F. Looney. 215 photographs: panoramas, street scenes, landmarks, President-elect Lincoln's visit, 1876 Centennial Exposition, much more. 230pp. 8⅞ × 11¾.
23345-6 Pa. $9.95

PRELUDE TO MATHEMATICS, W.W. Sawyer. Noted mathematician's lively, stimulating account of non-Euclidean geometry, matrices, determinants, group theory, other topics. Emphasis on novel, striking aspects. 224pp. 5⅜ × 8½.
24401-6 Pa. $4.50

ADVENTURES WITH A MICROSCOPE, Richard Headstrom. 59 adventures with clothing fibers, protozoa, ferns and lichens, roots and leaves, much more. 142 illustrations. 232pp. 5⅜ × 8½. 23471-1 Pa. $3.95

IDENTIFYING ANIMAL TRACKS: MAMMALS, BIRDS, AND OTHER ANIMALS OF THE EASTERN UNITED STATES, Richard Headstrom. For hunters, naturalists, scouts, nature-lovers. Diagrams of tracks, tips on identification. 128pp. 5⅜ × 8. 24442-3 Pa. $3.50

VICTORIAN FASHIONS AND COSTUMES FROM HARPER'S BAZAR, 1867-1898, edited by Stella Blum. Day costumes, evening wear, sports clothes, shoes, hats, other accessories in over 1,000 detailed engravings. 320pp. 9⅜ × 12¼.
22990-4 Pa. $10.95

EVERYDAY FASHIONS OF THE TWENTIES AS PICTURED IN SEARS AND OTHER CATALOGS, edited by Stella Blum. Actual dress of the Roaring Twenties, with text by Stella Blum. Over 750 illustrations, captions. 156pp. 9 × 12.
24134-3 Pa. $8.95

HALL OF FAME BASEBALL CARDS, edited by Bert Randolph Sugar. Cy Young, Ted Williams, Lou Gehrig, and many other Hall of Fame greats on 92 full-color, detachable reprints of early baseball cards. No duplication of cards with *Classic Baseball Cards.* 16pp. 8¼ × 11. 23624-2 Pa. $3.50

THE ART OF HAND LETTERING, Helm Wotzkow. Course in hand lettering, Roman, Gothic, Italic, Block, Script. Tools, proportions, optical aspects, individual variation. Very quality conscious. Hundreds of specimens. 320pp. 5⅜ × 8½.
21797-3 Pa. $5.95

HOW THE OTHER HALF LIVES, Jacob A. Riis. Journalistic record of filth, degradation, upward drive in New York immigrant slums, shops, around 1900. New edition includes 100 original Riis photos, monuments of early photography. 233pp. 10 × 7⅞. 22012-5 Pa. $9.95

CHINA AND ITS PEOPLE IN EARLY PHOTOGRAPHS, John Thomson. In 200 black-and-white photographs of exceptional quality photographic pioneer Thomson captures the mountains, dwellings, monuments and people of 19th-century China. 272pp. 9⅜ × 12¼. 24393-1 Pa. $13.95

GODEY COSTUME PLATES IN COLOR FOR DECOUPAGE AND FRAMING, edited by Eleanor Hasbrouk Rawlings. 24 full-color engravings depicting 19th-century Parisian haute couture. Printed on one side only. 56pp. 8¼ × 11. 23879-2 Pa. $3.95

ART NOUVEAU STAINED GLASS PATTERN BOOK, Ed Sibbett, Jr. 104 projects using well-known themes of Art Nouveau: swirling forms, florals, peacocks, and sensuous women. 60pp. 8¼ × 11. 23577-7 Pa. $3.95

QUICK AND EASY PATCHWORK ON THE SEWING MACHINE: Susan Aylsworth Murwin and Suzzy Payne. Instructions, diagrams show exactly how to machine sew 12 quilts. 48pp. of templates. 50 figures. 80pp. 8¼ × 11. 23770-2 Pa. $3.95

THE STANDARD BOOK OF QUILT MAKING AND COLLECTING, Marguerite Ickis. Full information, full-sized patterns for making 46 traditional quilts, also 150 other patterns. 483 illustrations. 273pp. 6⅞ × 9⅝. 20582-7 Pa. $5.95

LETTERING AND ALPHABETS, J. Albert Cavanagh. 85 complete alphabets lettered in various styles; instructions for spacing, roughs, brushwork. 121pp. 8¾ × 8. 20053-1 Pa. $3.95

LETTER FORMS: 110 COMPLETE ALPHABETS, Frederick Lambert. 110 sets of capital letters; 16 lower case alphabets; 70 sets of numbers and other symbols. 110pp. 8⅛ × 11. 22872-X Pa. $4.50

ORCHIDS AS HOUSE PLANTS, Rebecca Tyson Northen. Grow cattleyas and many other kinds of orchids—in a window, in a case, or under artificial light. 63 illustrations. 148pp. 5⅜ × 8½. 23261-1 Pa. $2.95

THE MUSHROOM HANDBOOK, Louis C.C. Krieger. Still the best popular handbook. Full descriptions of 259 species, extremely thorough text, poisons, folklore, etc. 32 color plates; 126 other illustrations. 560pp. 5⅜ × 8½. 21861-9 Pa. $8.50

THE DORÉ BIBLE ILLUSTRATIONS, Gustave Doré. All wonderful, detailed plates: Adam and Eve, Flood, Babylon, life of Jesus, etc. Brief King James text with each plate. 241 plates. 241pp. 9 × 12. 23004-X Pa. $8.95

THE BOOK OF KELLS: Selected Plates in Full Color, edited by Blanche Cirker. 32 full-page plates from greatest manuscript-icon of early Middle Ages. Fantastic, mysterious. Publisher's Note. Captions. 32pp. 9¾ × 12¼. 24345-1 Pa. $4.50

THE PERFECT WAGNERITE, George Bernard Shaw. Brilliant criticism of the Ring Cycle, with provocative interpretation of politics, economic theories behind the Ring. 136pp. 5⅜ × 8½. (EUK) 21707-8 Pa. $3.95

THE RIME OF THE ANCIENT MARINER, Gustave Doré, S.T. Coleridge. Doré's finest work, 34 plates capture moods, subtleties of poem. Full text. 77pp. 9¼ × 12. 22305-1 Pa. $4.95

SONGS OF INNOCENCE, William Blake. The first and most popular of Blake's famous "Illuminated Books," in a facsimile edition reproducing all 31 brightly colored plates. Additional printed text of each poem. 64pp. 5¼ × 7.
22764-2 Pa. $3.50

AN INTRODUCTION TO INFORMATION THEORY, J.R. Pierce. Second (1980) edition of most impressive non-technical account available. Encoding, entropy, noisy channel, related areas, etc. 320pp. 5⅜ × 8½. 24061-4 Pa. $5.95

THE DIVINE PROPORTION: A STUDY IN MATHEMATICAL BEAUTY, H.E. Huntley. "Divine proportion" or "golden ratio" in poetry, Pascal's triangle, philosophy, psychology, music, mathematical figures, etc. Excellent bridge between science and art. 58 figures. 185pp. 5⅜ × 8½. 22254-3 Pa. $4.50

THE DOVER NEW YORK WALKING GUIDE: From the Battery to Wall Street, Mary J. Shapiro. Superb inexpensive guide to historic buildings and locales in lower Manhattan: Trinity Church, Bowling Green, more. Complete Text; maps. 36 illustrations. 48pp. 3⅞ × 9¼. 24225-0 Pa. $2.50

NEW YORK THEN AND NOW, Edward B. Watson, Edmund V. Gillon, Jr. 83 important Manhattan sites: on facing pages early photographs (1875-1925) and 1976 photos by Gillon. 172 illustrations. 171pp. 9¼ × 10. 23361-8 Pa. $9.95

HISTORIC COSTUME IN PICTURES, Braun & Schneider. Over 1450 costumed figures from dawn of civilization to end of 19th century. English captions. 125 plates. 256pp. 8⅜ × 11¼. 23150-X Pa. $7.95

VICTORIAN AND EDWARDIAN FASHION: A Photographic Survey, Alison Gernsheim. First fashion history completely illustrated by contemporary photographs. Full text plus 235 photos, 1840-1914, in which many celebrities appear. 240pp. 6½ × 9¼. 24205-6 Pa. $6.00

CHARTED CHRISTMAS DESIGNS FOR COUNTED CROSS-STITCH AND OTHER NEEDLECRAFTS, Lindberg Press. Charted designs for 45 beautiful needlecraft projects with many yuletide and wintertime motifs. 48pp. 8¼ × 11. (EDNS) 24356-7 Pa. $2.50

101 FOLK DESIGNS FOR COUNTED CROSS-STITCH AND OTHER NEEDLE-CRAFTS, Carter Houck. 101 authentic charted folk designs in a wide array of lovely representations with many suggestions for effective use. 48pp. 8¼ × 11.
24369-9 Pa. $2.25

FIVE ACRES AND INDEPENDENCE, Maurice G. Kains. Great back-to-the-land classic explains basics of self-sufficient farming. The one book to get. 95 illustrations. 397pp. 5⅜ × 8½. 20974-1 Pa. $6.50

A MODERN HERBAL, Margaret Grieve. Much the fullest, most exact, most useful compilation of herbal material. Gigantic alphabetical encyclopedia, from aconite to zedoary, gives botanical information, medical properties, folklore, economic uses, and much else. Indispensable to serious reader. 161 illustrations. 888pp. 6½ × 9¼. (Available in U.S. only) 22798-7, 22799-5 Pa., Two-vol. set $17.00

DECORATIVE NAPKIN FOLDING FOR BEGINNERS, Lillian Oppenheimer and Natalie Epstein. 22 different napkin folds in the shape of a heart, clown's hat, love knot, etc. 63 drawings. 48pp. 8¼ × 11. 23797-4 Pa. $2.25

DECORATIVE LABELS FOR HOME CANNING, PRESERVING, AND OTHER HOUSEHOLD AND GIFT USES, Theodore Menten. 128 gummed, perforated labels, beautifully printed in 2 colors. 12 versions. Adhere to metal, glass, wood, ceramics. 24pp. 8¼ × 11. 23219-0 Pa. $3.50

EARLY AMERICAN STENCILS ON WALLS AND FURNITURE, Janet Waring. Thorough coverage of 19th-century folk art: techniques, artifacts, surviving specimens. 166 illustrations, 7 in color. 147pp. of text. 7⅞ × 10¾. 21906-2 Pa. $9.95

AMERICAN ANTIQUE WEATHERVANES, A.B. & W.T. Westervelt. Extensively illustrated 1883 catalog exhibiting over 550 copper weathervanes and finials. Excellent primary source by one of the principal manufacturers. 104pp. 6⅛ × 9¼. 24396-6 Pa. $3.95

ART STUDENTS' ANATOMY, Edmond J. Farris. Long favorite in art schools. Basic elements, common positions, actions. Full text, 158 illustrations. 159pp. 5⅜ × 8½. 20744-7 Pa. $3.95

BRIDGMAN'S LIFE DRAWING, George B. Bridgman. More than 500 drawings and text teach you to abstract the body into its major masses. Also specific areas of anatomy. 192pp. 6½ × 9¼. 22710-3 Pa. $4.50

COMPLETE PRELUDES AND ETUDES FOR SOLO PIANO, Frederic Chopin. All 26 Preludes, all 27 Etudes by greatest composer of piano music. Authoritative Paderewski edition. 224pp. 9 × 12. (Available in U.S. only) 24052-5 Pa. $7.50

PIANO MUSIC 1888-1905, Claude Debussy. Deux Arabesques, Suite Bergamesque, Masques, 1st series of Images, etc. 9 others, in corrected editions. 175pp. 9⅜ × 12¼. 22771-5 Pa. $6.95

TEDDY BEAR IRON-ON TRANSFER PATTERNS, Ted Menten. 80 iron-on transfer patterns of male and female Teddys in a wide variety of activities, poses, sizes. 48pp. 8¼ × 11. 24596-9 Pa. $2.25

A PICTURE HISTORY OF THE BROOKLYN BRIDGE, M.J. Shapiro. Profusely illustrated account of greatest engineering achievement of 19th century. 167 rare photos & engravings recall construction, human drama. Extensive, detailed text. 122pp. 8¼ × 11. 24403-2 Pa. $7.95

NEW YORK IN THE THIRTIES, Berenice Abbott. Noted photographer's fascinating study shows new buildings that have become famous and old sights that have disappeared forever. 97 photographs. 97pp. 11⅜ × 10. 22967-X Pa. $7.50

MATHEMATICAL TABLES AND FORMULAS, Robert D. Carmichael and Edwin R. Smith. Logarithms, sines, tangents, trig functions, powers, roots, reciprocals, exponential and hyperbolic functions, formulas and theorems. 269pp. 5⅜ × 8½. 60111-0 Pa. $4.95

HANDBOOK OF MATHEMATICAL FUNCTIONS WITH FORMULAS, GRAPHS, AND MATHEMATICAL TABLES, edited by Milton Abramowitz and Irene A. Stegun. Vast compendium: 29 sets of tables, some to as high as 20 places. 1,046pp. 8 × 10½. 61272-4 Pa. $21.95

REASON IN ART, George Santayana. Renowned philosopher's provocative, seminal treatment of basis of art in instinct and experience. Volume Four of *The Life of Reason*. 230pp. 5⅜ × 8. 24358-3 Pa. $4.50

LANGUAGE, TRUTH AND LOGIC, Alfred J. Ayer. Famous, clear introduction to Vienna, Cambridge schools of Logical Positivism. Role of philosophy, elimination of metaphysics, nature of analysis, etc. 160pp. 5⅜ × 8½. (USCO) 20010-8 Pa. $2.95

BASIC ELECTRONICS, U.S. Bureau of Naval Personnel. Electron tubes, circuits, antennas, AM, FM, and CW transmission and receiving, etc. 560 illustrations. 567pp. 6½ × 9¼. 21076-6 Pa. $9.95

THE ART DECO STYLE, edited by Theodore Menten. Furniture, jewelry, metalwork, ceramics, fabrics, lighting fixtures, interior decors, exteriors, graphics from pure French sources. Over 400 photographs. 183pp. 8⅜ × 11¼. 22824-X Pa. $7.95

THE FOUR BOOKS OF ARCHITECTURE, Andrea Palladio. 16th-century classic covers classical architectural remains, Renaissance revivals, classical orders, etc. 1738 Ware English edition. 216 plates. 110pp. of text. 9½ × 12¾. 21308-0 Pa. $11.95

THE WIT AND HUMOR OF OSCAR WILDE, edited by Alvin Redman. More than 1000 ripostes, paradoxes, wisecracks: Work is the curse of the drinking classes, I can resist everything except temptations, etc. 258pp. 5⅜ × 8½. 20602-5 Pa. $4.50

THE DEVIL'S DICTIONARY, Ambrose Bierce. Barbed, bitter, brilliant witticisms in the form of a dictionary. Best, most ferocious satire America has produced. 145pp. 5⅜ × 8½. 20487-1 Pa. $2.95

ERTÉ'S FASHION DESIGNS, Erté. 210 black-and-white inventions from *Harper's Bazar*, 1918-32, plus 8pp. full-color covers. Captions. 88pp. 9 × 12. 24203-X Pa. $7.95

ERTÉ GRAPHICS, Erté. Collection of striking color graphics: *Seasons, Alphabet, Numerals, Aces* and *Precious Stones*. 50 plates, including 4 on covers. 48pp. 9⅜ × 12¼. 23580-7 Pa. $6.95

PAPER FOLDING FOR BEGINNERS, William D. Murray and Francis J. Rigney. Clearest book for making origami sail boats, roosters, frogs that move legs, etc. 40 projects. More than 275 illustrations. 94pp. 5⅜ × 8½. 20713-7 Pa. $2.50

ORIGAMI FOR THE ENTHUSIAST, John Montroll. Fish, ostrich, peacock, squirrel, rhinoceros, Pegasus, 19 other intricate subjects. Instructions. Diagrams. 128pp. 9 × 12. 23799-0 Pa. $5.95

CROCHETING NOVELTY POT HOLDERS, edited by Linda Macho. 64 useful, whimsical pot holders feature kitchen themes, animals, flowers, other novelties. Surprisingly easy to crochet. Complete instructions. 48pp. 8¼ × 11. 24296-X Pa. $1.95

CROCHETING DOILIES, edited by Rita Weiss. Irish Crochet, Jewel, Star Wheel, Vanity Fair and more. Also luncheon and console sets, runners and centerpieces. 51 illustrations. 48pp. 8¼ × 11. 23424-X Pa. $2.75

YUCATAN BEFORE AND AFTER THE CONQUEST, Diego de Landa. Only significant account of Yucatan written in the early post-Conquest era. Translated by William Gates. Over 120 illustrations. 162pp. 5⅜ × 8½. 23622-6 Pa. $3.95

ORNATE PICTORIAL CALLIGRAPHY, E.A. Lupfer. Complete instructions, over 150 examples help you create magnificent "flourishes" from which beautiful animals and objects gracefully emerge. 8⅛ × 11. 21957-7 Pa. $3.50

DOLLY DINGLE PAPER DOLLS, Grace Drayton. Cute chubby children by same artist who did Campbell Kids. Rare plates from 1910s. 30 paper dolls and over 100 outfits reproduced in full color. 32pp. 9¼ × 12¼. 23711-7 Pa. $3.50

CURIOUS GEORGE PAPER DOLLS IN FULL COLOR, H. A. Rey, Kathy Allert. Naughty little monkey-hero of children's books in two doll figures, plus 48 full-color costumes: pirate, Indian chief, fireman, more. 32pp. 9¼ × 12¼. 24386-9 Pa. $3.50

GERMAN: HOW TO SPEAK AND WRITE IT, Joseph Rosenberg. Like *French, How to Speak and Write It.* Very rich modern course, with a wealth of pictorial material. 330 illustrations. 384pp. 5⅜ × 8½. 20271-2 Pa. $4.95

CATS AND KITTENS: 24 Ready-to-Mail Color Photo Postcards, D. Holby. Handsome collection; feline in a variety of adorable poses. Identifications. 12pp. on postcard stock. 8¼ × 11. 24469-5 Pa. $2.95

MARILYN MONROE PAPER DOLLS, Tom Tierney. 31 full-color designs on heavy stock, from *The Asphalt Jungle, Gentlemen Prefer Blondes,* 22 others. 1 doll. 16 plates. 32pp. 9⅜ × 12¼. 23769-9 Pa. $3.95

FUNDAMENTALS OF LAYOUT, F.H. Wills. All phases of layout design discussed and illustrated in 121 illustrations. Indispensable as student's text or handbook for professional. 124pp. 8⅛ × 11. 21279-3 Pa. $4.50

FANTASTIC SUPER STICKERS, Ed Sibbett, Jr. 75 colorful pressure-sensitive stickers. Peel off and place for a touch of pizzazz: clowns, penguins, teddy bears, etc. Full color. 16pp. 8¼ × 11. 24471-7 Pa. $3.50

LABELS FOR ALL OCCASIONS, Ed Sibbett, Jr. 6 labels each of 16 different designs—baroque, art nouveau, art deco, Pennsylvania Dutch, etc.—in full color. 24pp. 8¼ × 11. 23688-9 Pa. $3.95

HOW TO CALCULATE QUICKLY: RAPID METHODS IN BASIC MATHEMATICS, Henry Sticker. Addition, subtraction, multiplication, division, checks, etc. More than 8000 problems, solutions. 185pp. 5 × 7¼. 20295-X Pa. $2.95

THE CAT COLORING BOOK, Karen Baldauski. Handsome, realistic renderings of 40 splendid felines, from American shorthair to exotic types. 44 plates. Captions. 48pp. 8¼ × 11. 24011-8 Pa. $2.50

THE TALE OF PETER RABBIT, Beatrix Potter. The inimitable Peter's terrifying adventure in Mr. McGregor's garden, with all 27 wonderful, full-color Potter illustrations. 55pp. 4¼ × 5½. (Available in U.S. only) 22827-4 Pa. $1.75

BASIC ELECTRICITY, U.S. Bureau of Naval Personnel. Batteries, circuits, conductors, AC and DC, inductance and capacitance, generators, motors, transformers, amplifiers, etc. 349 illustrations. 448pp. 6½ × 9¼. 20973-3 Pa. $7.95

SOURCE BOOK OF MEDICAL HISTORY, edited by Logan Clendening, M.D. Original accounts ranging from Ancient Egypt and Greece to discovery of X-rays: Galen, Pasteur, Lavoisier, Harvey, Parkinson, others. 685pp. 5⅜ × 8½.
20621-1 Pa. $11.95

THE ROSE AND THE KEY, J.S. Lefanu. Superb mystery novel from Irish master. Dark doings among an ancient and aristocratic English family. Well-drawn characters; capital suspense. Introduction by N. Donaldson. 448pp. 5⅜ × 8½.
24377-X Pa. $6.95

SOUTH WIND, Norman Douglas. Witty, elegant novel of ideas set on languorous Meditterranean island of Nepenthe. Elegant prose, glittering epigrams, mordant satire. 1917 masterpiece. 416pp. 5⅜ × 8½. (Available in U.S. only)
24361-3 Pa. $5.95

RUSSELL'S CIVIL WAR PHOTOGRAPHS, Capt. A.J. Russell. 116 rare Civil War Photos: Bull Run, Virginia campaigns, bridges, railroads, Richmond, Lincoln's funeral car. Many never seen before. Captions. 128pp. 9⅜ × 12¼.
24283-8 Pa. $7.95

PHOTOGRAPHS BY MAN RAY: 105 Works, 1920-1934. Nudes, still lifes, landscapes, women's faces, celebrity portraits (Dali, Matisse, Picasso, others), rayographs. Reprinted from rare gravure edition. 128pp. 9⅜ × 12¼.
23842-3 Pa. $8.95

STAR NAMES: THEIR LORE AND MEANING, Richard H. Allen. Star names, the zodiac, constellations: folklore and literature associated with heavens. The basic book of its field, fascinating reading. 563pp. 5⅜ × 8½.   21079-0 Pa. $7.95

BURNHAM'S CELESTIAL HANDBOOK, Robert Burnham, Jr. Thorough guide to the stars beyond our solar system. Exhaustive treatment. Alphabetical by constellation: Andromeda to Cetus in Vol. 1; Chamaeleon to Orion in Vol. 2; and Pavo to Vulpecula in Vol. 3. Hundreds of illustrations. Index in Vol. 3. 2000pp. 6⅛ × 9¼.   23567-X, 23568-8, 23673-0 Pa. Three-vol. set $37.85

THE ART NOUVEAU STYLE BOOK OF ALPHONSE MUCHA, Alphonse Mucha. All 72 plates from *Documents Decoratifs* in original color. Stunning, essential work of Art Nouveau. 80pp. 9⅜ × 12¼.   24044-4 Pa. $8.95

DESIGNS BY ERTE; FASHION DRAWINGS AND ILLUSTRATIONS FROM "HARPER'S BAZAR," Erte. 310 fabulous line drawings and 14 *Harper's Bazar* covers, 8 in full color. Erte's exotic temptresses with tassels, fur muffs, long trains, coifs, more. 129pp. 9⅜ × 12¼.   23397-9 Pa. $8.95

HISTORY OF STRENGTH OF MATERIALS, Stephen P. Timoshenko. Excellent historical survey of the strength of materials with many references to the theories of elasticity and structure. 245 figures. 452pp. 5⅜ × 8½.   61187-6 Pa. $9.95

Prices subject to change without notice.

Available at your book dealer or write for free catalog to Dept. GI, Dover Publications, Inc., 31 East 2nd St. Mineola, N.Y. 11501. Dover publishes more than 175 books each year on science, elementary and advanced mathematics, biology, music, art, literary history, social sciences and other areas.